2nd Edition

Family and Friends 3

Workbook

Liz Driscoll

OXFORD
UNIVERSITY PRESS

OXFORD
UNIVERSITY PRESS

Great Clarendon Street, Oxford, OX2 6DP, United Kingdom

Oxford University Press is a department of the University of Oxford.
It furthers the University's objective of excellence in research, scholarship,
and education by publishing worldwide. Oxford is a registered trade
mark of Oxford University Press in the UK and in certain other countries

ISBN: 978 0 19 480864 4   Pack
ISBN: 978 0 19 480871 2   Workbook (with Online Practice)
ISBN: 978 0 19 480924 5   Online Practice Student Access Code Card

Printed in China

This book is printed on paper from certified and well-managed sources

ACKNOWLEDGEMENTS

Illustrations by: Adrian Barclay (Beehive Illustration) pp.5, 9, 10 (Ex1), 15,
16 (Ex1), 21, 22 (Ex1), 31, 32 (Ex1), 37, 38 (Ex1), 43, 44 (Ex1), 53, 54 (Ex1), 59,
60 (Ex1, 2), 65, 72 (Ex1, 2), 75, 76 (Ex1), 81, 82 (Ex1), 87, 88 (Ex1), 95 (Ex4), 97,
103, 104 (Ex1), 109, 110 (Ex2); Kathy Baxendale pp.25, 63; Jared Beckstrand
pp.6, 10 (Ex3), 16 (Ex3), 22 (Ex2), 32 (Ex2), 38 (Ex2), 44 (Ex2), 54 (Ex3), 60 (Ex3),
62 (Ex2), 76 (Ex2), 82 (Ex2), 88 (Ex3), 98, 104 (Ex2), 110 (Ex3); Judy Brown
pp.26, 48, 70, 92, 114, 122, 123; Simon Clare pp.11, 17, 23, 33, 39, 45, 55, 61,
67, 77, 83, 89, 99, 105, 111; Steve Cox pp.13, 78 (Ex2); James Elston p.4; Paul
Gibbs pp.40 (Ex2), 41; John Haslam pp.12 (Ex2), 28 (Ex1), 29 (Ex4), 47, 50 (Ex1),
51 (Ex4), 73 (Ex4), 84, 94 (Ex1, 2), 116 (Ex1), 117 (Ex4); Andrew Hennessey pp.7,
8, 12 (Ex1), 14, 18, 19, 20, 24, 30, 34, 36, 40 (Ex1), 42, 52, 56 (Ex1), 58f, 62 (Ex1),
64, 68, 74, 78 (Ex1), 80, 86, 90 (Ex1), 96, 102, 106, 108; Carl Pearce (Advocate
Art) pp.35, 91, 100, 101, 113; Lesley Vamos (Andrea Brown Literary Agency)
pp.118; Ignatios Varsos p.66.

Commissioned photography by: David Jordan p.46.

Oxford University Press DVD stills: pp.27, 49, 71, 93, 115

*The Publishers would like to thank the following for their kind permission to reproduce
photographs and other copyright material*: **Alamy** pp.085 (Nabatean coin/Ancient
Art & Architecture Collection Ltd), 090 (wedding/ClassicStock), 112 (Barcelona
Zoo/Apix), 118 (Oxford High Street/Loop Images Ltd), 119 (London
Marathon/Ashok Saxena), 120 (girl in snow with hat/UpperCut Images);
Getty pp.120 (boy tennis serve/Olga Solovei); **iStock** pp.090 (young girl/
HultonArchive); **Shutterstock** pp.090 (old woman/Martina Ebel), 118 (girl/
Monkey Business Images).

Cover illustration by: James Elston

Contents

My family

Lesson One

1 Find and circle the family words in red and the numbers in blue.

Then write two lists.

family words
uncle

t	h	r	e	e	i	g	h	t
b	r	o	t	h	e	r	s	w
s	i	s	t	e	r	a	i	o
e	c	o	u	s	i	n	x	★
v	u	g	r	a	n	d	m	a
e	n	f	i	v	e	p	u	u
n	c	o	n	e	★	a	m	n
★	l	u	n	i	n	e	★	t
★	e	r	d	a	d	★	★	★

numbers
one

2 Look at Max and Holly's family photos. Write the sentences.

1	This is my sister.
2	
3	
4	
5	

6	
7	
8	
9	
10	

1 Circle the correct words.

1 **Giraffes** / **Goats** are taller than lions.
2 **Snakes** / **Cows** are bigger than goats.
3 **Hens** / **Elephants** are smaller than sheep.
4 **Horses** / **Cows** are faster than sheep.

2 Write.

1 Zebras are _____taller_____ (tall) than sheep.
2 Elephants are _____ (big) than cows.
3 Hens are _____ (small) than dogs.
4 Horses are _____ (big) than donkeys.

3 Write *was* or *were*.

Yesterday, James and Polly [1] _____were_____ at the beach with their mum and dad.
It [2] _____ sunny. The children [3] _____ very happy.
At twelve o'clock, they [4] _____ hungry. Mum [5] _____ hot.
She [6] _____ thirsty, too. Dad [7] _____ tired.

Lesson Three

1 Complete the words.

Twelve months in a year

¹ January , ² F_____ ,
³ March and ⁴ A_____ ,
⁵ M_____ , ⁶ June ,
⁷ J_____ , then ⁸ August
and ⁹ S_____ ,
¹⁰ October , ¹¹ N_____
and ¹² D_____ ,
Twelve months in a year!

2 Write the next month.

1 January, February, _____ March _____

2 September, October, _____

3 May, June, _____

4 December, January, _____

5 July, August, _____

6 February, March, _____

3 Write about you.

When is your birthday? _____

How old are you? _____

When is your mum's birthday? _____

What is your favourite month? _____

1 Match.

a **30**

b **100**

forty-five ☐
thirty ☐ a
ten ☐
thirty-nine ☐
fifty ☐
one hundred ☐
sixty ☐
twenty-two ☐

c **50**

d **45**

e **10**

f **22**

g **39**

h **60**

2 Write the next number.

1 twenty-one, twenty-two, _twenty-three_

2 eight, nine, _____

3 thirty-four, thirty-five, _____

4 sixty-seven, sixty-eight, _____

5 thirteen, fourteen, _____

6 ninety-eight, ninety-nine, _____

3 Write in words and complete the sums.

1 10 + 70 = ?   _ten and seventy is eighty_

2 40 + 50 = ?   _____

3 30 + ? = 70   _____

4 20 + ? = 100 _____

5 60 + ? = 90   _____

Lesson One Words

1 Write.

| Egypt | the UK | Spain | Russia | Thailand | Australia | the USA | Brazil |

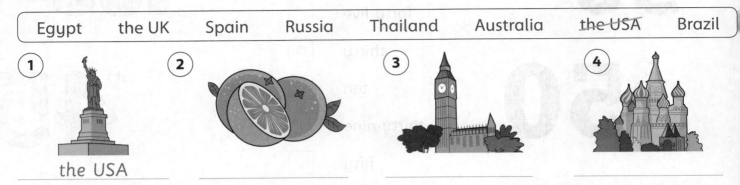

1. the USA
2.
3.
4.

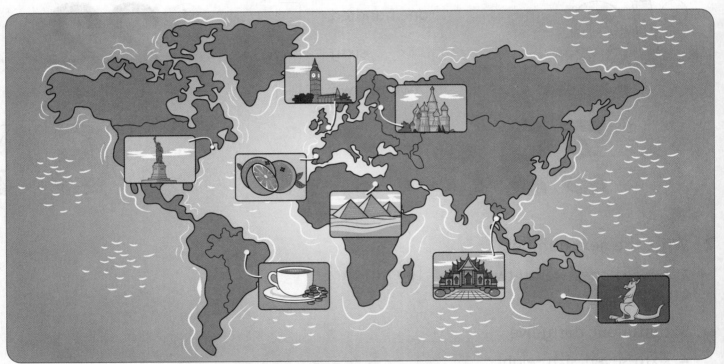

5.
6.
7.
8.

2 Write about you.

My name's _____ .

I'm from _____ .

1 Tick (✓) the correct sentences.

1 Lola is eight.

    She's from Spain.   ✓
    They're from Spain.   ☐

2 My name's Sam.

    I'm from the USA.   ☐
    You're from the USA.   ☐

3 You and Pedro are friends.

    They're from Brazil.   ☐
    You're from Brazil.   ☐

4 Mahmood and Ahmed are cousins.

    She's from Egypt.   ☐
    They're from Egypt.   ☐

5 Lee is eight years old.

    He's from Thailand.   ☐
    We're from Thailand.   ☐

6 Jenny and I are cousins.

    She's from Australia.   ☐
    We're from Australia.   ☐

2 Order the letters and write the answers. **G** Grammar Time! page 124

saRusi

ygtpE

liBzra

apSin

1 Read and write.

1 Jane is eight. She's from ___the UK___ .

2 Tom is _____ . He's from Australia.

3 Ellie is nine. She's from _____ .

4 Carl is _____ . He's from the USA.

5 Lisa is _____ . She's from the UK.

6 Jack is ten. He's from _____ .

2 Write about you and your friends.

I'm _____ . I'm from _____ .

_____ is _____ . _____ .

_____ is _____ . _____ .

3 Write. | from   I'm   He's   It's   ~~are you~~   meet   you   are |

Where are you from?

Where [1] ___are you___ from?

[2] _____ from the UK.

Hello, hello,

How are [3] _____ today?

This is my friend.

[4] _____ from the USA.

Hello, hello,

How [5] _____ you today?

I'm [6] _____ Brazil.

[7] _____ nice to meet you!

Hello, hello,

Nice to [8] _____ you, too.

1 **Complete the words.** | cr   dr   sp   ~~sn~~   pl |

__sn__ake   ____ay   ____ayon   ____ink   ____oon

2 **Match the sound with the correct picture. Circle.**

1

2

3

4

5

3 **Write.** | draw   play   ~~drink~~   crayon   spoon |

We ^{1}____drink____ from a cup.
We eat with a ^{2}_____.
We ^{3}_____ with a
^{4}_____.
We ^{5}_____ all afternoon.

Reading

1 Complete the words. Number the words to match the pictures.

4	g a r d e n
	w _ _ _ _ _ r
	_ _ r _ g
	s _ _ _ o _
	_ _ m m _ _
	_ _ t _ m _

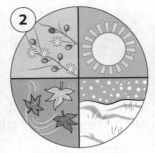

2 Match the sentences with the pictures. Write *a* or *b*.

1 Bruno the bear isn't awake.   b

2 The other animals are asleep.

3 The animals are awake, but where's Bruno?

4 Bruno isn't happy because he's alone.

5 Bruno isn't in his home.

6 It's hot and there are lots of flowers.

7 It isn't warm and sunny.

8 The animals are happy because it's summer.

Writing

1 Write the questions with capital letters. Then answer the questions.

1 is leo from egypt?

Is Leo from Egypt? _No, he isn't._

2 are you from the usa?

_____ _____

3 is your birthday in august?

_____ _____

4 is holly from australia?

_____ _____

5 is your family from spain?

_____ _____

6 is your birthday in june?

_____ _____

 **My writing**

2 Choose and write.

My name is Katya. I'm from _____ (**the UK / the USA**).
I'm ten. My favourite season is _____ (**autumn / spring**).

My name is _____ (**Brett / Greg**). I'm from Australia.
I'm _____ (**eight / nine**). My favourite season is summer.

3 Write about you.

My name _____. I'm _____.
I'm _____. My _____

_____.

Lesson One Words

1 Number the picture.

1	fish
2	skateboard
3	take photos
4	play chess
5	read comics
6	play basketball
7	do gymnastics
8	play volleyball

2 Write.

They play chess _____ every day.

_____ in the park.

_____ of their friends.

_____ in the evenings.

1 **Read and write *T* (true) or *F* (false).** G Grammar Time! page 124

1 He likes skateboarding. **F**

2 They like playing chess.

3 I don't like reading comics.

4 We don't like fishing.

2 **Write.** G Grammar Time! page 124

1 I _don't like taking_ photos.

2 We _____ kites.

3 My brother _____ _____ comics.

4 My sister _____ _____ chess.

5 I _____ .

6 I _____ .

Do you like fishing? No, I don't. **Unit 2**

1 **Match the questions and the answers.**

1 Do Max and Jerry like fishing?   d   a Yes, he does.

2 Does Fred like fishing?   ☐   b No, they don't.

3 Do Fred and Max like skateboarding? ☐   c No, he doesn't.

4 Does Jerry like skateboarding?   ☐   d Yes, they do.

2 **Write about you. Complete the questions and circle your answers.**

1 Do you like reading comics?   Yes, I do. / No, I don't.

2 Do you like climbing?   Yes, I do. / No, I don't.

3 Do you _____ gymnastics? Yes, I do. / No, I don't.

4 Do you _____ chess?   Yes, I do. / No, I don't.

3 **Write.**   photos   I   like   ~~likes~~   drawing   playing   we   chess

I'm happy it's the weekend!

Dad ¹_____likes_____ playing basketball,

And he likes playing ²_____.

Mum likes ³_____ tennis,

But I ⁴_____ fishing best!

Mum likes ⁵_____ pictures,

And ⁶_____ like drawing, too.

Dad likes taking ⁷_____,

So ⁸_____ 've got lots to do!

1 **Circle the two words that sound the same.**

1 (space)   cube   bike   (face)   2 stone   June   rope   lake

3 line   flute   gate   white   4 home   cube   plane   tube

5 face   nose   bone   time   6 kite   race   June   nine

2 **Complete the words.**

There's a n _o s e_ on my f __ c __ .

I like riding my b __ k __ in J __ n __ .

The c __ b __ has got six f __ c __ s.

The k __ t __ is flying into sp __ c __ .

3 **Write.** | face   cube   rope   space   ~~kite~~

Let's play together, me and you.
I've got a [1] _____ kite _____ ,
And a skipping [2] _____ , too.
I've got a [3] _____ ,
And a doll from [4] _____ .
Look. It's got a purple [5] _____ .

Skills Time!

Reading

1 Write.

1 _____paint_____

2 Read the Class Book and write *Kelly*, *Nuria* or *Ismail*.

1 __Kelly__ 's friends like watching DVDs.   2 _____ likes playing the guitar.

3 _____ 's friends like listening to music.   4 _____ likes watching football on TV.

5 _____ doesn't like sports.   6 _____ 's friend doesn't like basketball.

7 _____ likes playing the piano.   8 _____ and her friend like dancing.

9 _____ 's sisters love painting pictures.   10 _____ 's best friend likes volleyball.

Writing

1 Underline the full forms. Write the short forms.

1 <u>It is</u> hot in summer. _It's_   2 I have not got a sister. _____

3 We are not English. _____   4 I have got two cousins. _____

5 She has not got a comic. _____   6 He is from Brazil. _____

 My writing

2 Read the Class Book, page 18. Who are these emails for? Circle the correct names. Underline the short forms.

a

Hello **Kelly / Ismail / Nuria**!

My name's Kitty, I'm nine years old and I'm from the USA. I love cooking and I love music. My best friend Rosie and I like playing together – I like playing the guitar, and Rosie plays the piano. We want to play in a band! You also love music, and I want to be your email penfriend. Please write to me.

From Kitty

b

Hi **Kelly / Ismail / Nuria**!

I'm Felipe and I'm nine. I'm from Brazil. I like watching DVDs and listening to music, but I love doing sports! I like playing basketball and I love playing football on the beach with my friends. I'm in my school football team. You like watching football. Do you like playing football, too?

Please email me.

From Felipe

3 Choose a penfriend and write an email.

Hello / Hi _____

My name's / I'm _____.

I like _____
_____.

I don't like _____
_____.

Please _____

1 Match.

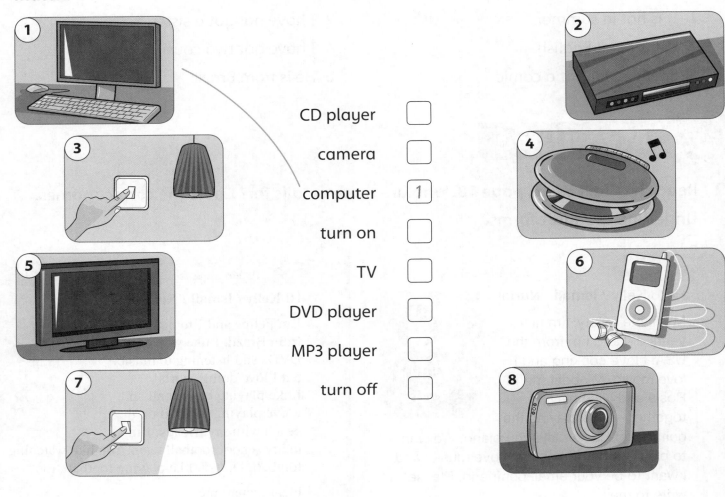

CD player ☐

camera ☐

computer ☐ 1

turn on ☐

TV ☐

DVD player ☐

MP3 player ☐

turn off ☐

2 Write.

turn off

1 Circle *our* or *their*. 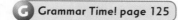 Grammar Time! page 125

1.  **Our / Their** computer is small.

2.  **Our / Their** camera is big.

3.  **Our / Their** computer is small.

4.  **Our / Their** CD player is small.

2 Write. Grammar Time! page 126

1.  Can I use your camera? (use) No, you can't .

2.  Can I _____? (watch) Yes, _____.

3.  _____ (listen) No, _____.

4.  _____ (read) Yes, _____.

1 **Write the questions.** 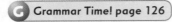 Grammar Time! page 126

1 Can you put on your coat, please? (put on)

2 Can you _____ _____? (close)

3 _____ (turn on)

4 _____ (open)

5 _____ (help)

6 _____ (turn off)

2 **Read the song in the Class Book. Write.**

It's rainy today

1 Can we watch a DVD?
2 _____ our new CD?
3 _____ TV?
4 _____ a show with me?
5 _____ out in the sun?
6 _____ with me all day?

1 Complete the crossword.

Down ↓

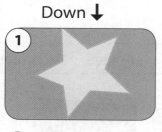

Across →

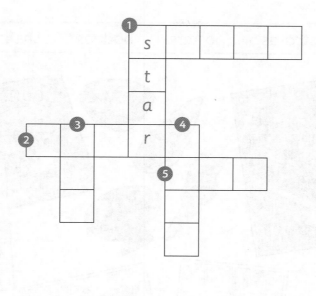

2 Write. car   shark   park   scarf

We're in the ¹_____car_____,

After playing in the ²_____.

I've got an orange ³_____,

I've got a toy ⁴_____.

3 Count and write.

1 There's one _____arm_____.

2 There are two _____.

3 There are three _____.

4 There are four _____.

5 There are five _____.

Skills Time!

Reading

1 Count and write. | postcards   posters   badges   shells   ~~stickers~~   comics |

1 There are six _____stickers_____ .

2 There are three _____ .

3 There are two _____ .

4 There are five _____ .

5 There are seven _____ .

6 There are four _____ .

2 Read the text in the Class Book. Circle the wrong words. Write the correct words.

1 Tony has got 60 (volleyball) stickers.   *football*

2 He gives his brother some of his stickers.   _____

3 There are 40 badges in Emily's collection.   _____

4 Her badges are on a poster on her bedroom wall. _____

5 Mark and his sister have got a collection of comics. _____

6 Their dad buys them two new comics every Monday. _____

Writing

1 **Write sentences. Use capital letters and punctuation marks.**

| , | ? | . |

1 canyouswitchonthecomputer   <u>Can you switch on the computer?</u>

2 ilikecookingshoppingandpainting   _____

3 haveyougotacamera   _____

4 ihavegotacomputeracameraandatv   _____

My writing

2 **Write the punctuation marks and circle the capital letters.** | , | ? | . |

Ⓘ've got a collection of postcards ¹ .

I've got 70 ² ___ I've got postcards

from the United States ³ ___ Spain ⁴ ___

Thailand ⁵ ___ Australia and from

my country ⁶ ___ My favourite

postcard is from Australia ⁷ ___

It's a kangaroo ⁸ ___ Have you got

any postcards ⁹ ___

70

3 **This is Tom's collection. Write about it.**

He's got a collection of _____ .

He's got _____ .

He's got _____ from

_____

_____ .

His favourite _____

_____ .

It's got pyramids on it.

30

Fluency Time! ①

Everyday English

1 Tick (✓) the correct sentences.

1 I love shopping.
So do I. I like cooking, too. ✓
Neither do I. But I like cooking. ☐

2 I love watching TV.
Neither do I. I prefer reading comics. ☐
I don't. I prefer reading comics. ☐

3 I don't like painting.
So do I. I like drawing, too. ☐
Neither do I. But I like drawing. ☐

4 I love skateboarding.
I don't. I prefer playing volleyball. ☐
Neither do I. I prefer playing volleyball. ☐

5 I like playing football.
Neither do I. But I like playing basketball. ☐
So do I. I like playing basketball, too. ☐

2 Write. | I don't | Neither do I | So do I | I don't |

1 I love doing gymnastics.
I don't.

2 I like taking photos.
_____

3 I don't like fishing.
_____

4 I love playing chess.
_____

1 Watch. Who likes each sport? Write *Tom*, *Anna*,
Tom and Anna or *N* (neither).

Tom

Anna

1 football _____ Tom _____

2 tennis _____

3 skateboarding _____

4 volleyball _____

2 What do they say? Match. Then number the pictures in order.

1 I love playing football. [c]

2 I prefer playing tennis. [ ]

3 I don't like skateboarding. [ ]

4 I like playing volleyball. [ ]

a Oh! I don't like tennis.

b Great! So do I!

c I don't.

d Neither do I.

1

3 What do you like? Talk with your friend. Use the phrases in the box.

I like …   I don't like …   I prefer …   So do I .   Neither do I.

1 Write the verbs.

1 He likes _____playing_____ the piano.
2 They like _____ volleyball.
3 She likes _____ photos.
4 She likes _____ fish pie.
5 She likes _____ comics.
6 They like _____ gymnastics.
7 He likes _____ family.

2 Circle the odd one out.

1 spring (chess) winter summer
3 cooking fishing autumn painting
5 tennis volleyball football season

2 DVD player TV MP3 player shopping
4 Australia CD player Brazil Egypt
6 cooking badges posters stickers

3 Circle the correct words.

1 (He) / I is from the USA.
3 Can I / you use your pen, please?
5 He / I like cooking.

2 She / They doesn't like fishing.
4 She / They are from Spain.
6 Can I / you help me with my homework?

4 Write *Can I* or *Can you*. Then answer the questions.

1. __Can you__ turn on the TV, please?
Yes, I can.

2. _____ paint, please?
_____

3. _____ open the door?
_____

4. _____ close the window?
_____

My work

My favourite story in Units 1–3 is _____

My favourite song in Units 1–3 is _____

My favourite unit in Units 1–3 is _____

I need to practise _____

My work in Units 1–3 is

 OK   **Good**   **Excellent**

Lesson One Words

1 Number the picture.

1	~~windsurf~~
2	sail
3	swim
4	kayak
5	surf
6	waterski
7	dive
8	snorkel

2 Write.

1 surf

2

3

4

5

6

7

8

1 **Read and tick (✓).** 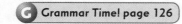 Grammar Time! page 126

They're sailing. ✓
They aren't sailing. ☐

She's surfing. ☐
She isn't surfing. ☐

They're kayaking. ☐
They aren't kayaking. ☐

He's waterskiing. ☐
He isn't waterskiing. ☐

2 **Write.**

| aren't   's   're   aren't   'm not   're   'm   isn't |

I'm swimming.
She isn't swimming.

We _____ windsurfing.
He _____ windsurfing.

I _____ snorkelling.
They _____ snorkelling.

We _____ surfing.
They _____ surfing.

1 Match.

1 She's listening to music. She isn't drinking a milkshake.   `c`

2 She's wearing a skirt. She isn't eating a sandwich.   ☐

3 She's reading a comic. She isn't wearing trousers.   ☐

4 She's eating a sandwich. She isn't wearing a skirt.   ☐

5 She's wearing trousers. She isn't reading a comic.   ☐

2 Read the song in the Class Book. Put the lines in the correct order.

At the beach!

a We're snorkelling and diving   ☐

b And we can swim and play   ☐

c We're sailing in our little boat   `9`

d We're playing in the sea   ☐

e We're swimming and we're surfing   ☐

f We're playing at the beach today   `1`

g We're having lots of fun   ☐

h We can windsurf at the beach   ☐

i And we're sitting in the sun   ☐

j We all like playing at the beach   `5`

k It's sunny here today   ☐

l There are lots of fish to see   ☐

1 **Complete the words.** | b | w | t | ~~sm~~ | m

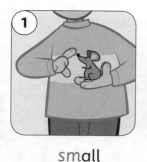

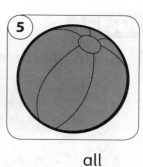

_sm_all   ____all   ____all   ____all   ____all

2 **Write.** | small | all | ~~mall~~ | tall | ball

I'm in a ¹ ____mall____ .
Some people are ² _____ ,
Some are ³ _____ .
I'm going to buy a ⁴ _____ .
I don't know which to buy.
I like them ⁵ _____ .

3 **Write words with _all_.**

1 We go to school ____all____ day.

2 We buy clothes in the _____ .

3 Giraffes are very _____ animals.

4 Let's play with a _____ in the park.

5 There's a cat on the _____ .

6 Australia isn't a _____ country.

7 I eat _____ my breakfast.

Skills Time!

Reading

1 Circle the correct words.

This river is **clean** / (**polluted**).

This park is **ugly** / **beautiful**.

This is **safe** / **dangerous**!

This river is **clean** / **polluted**.

This park is **ugly** / **beautiful**.

This is **safe** / **dangerous**!

2 Read the text in the Class Book. Write *T* (true) or *F* (false).

1 Dolphins live in the sea. T

2 They like playing with people. ___

3 Dolphins are dangerous. ___

4 They can breathe under water. ___

5 Dolphins call other dolphins with special sounds. ___

6 They like living in clean water. ___

Writing

1 **Write the verbs. Then answer the questions for you.** | Yes, I do.   No, I don't. |

1 Do you like _____writing_____ (write) emails?   _____

2 Do you like _____ (fly) kites?   _____

3 Do you like _____ (watch) TV?   _____

4 Do you like _____ (take) photos?   _____

 My writing

2 **Circle the correct words.**

We're at the ¹ **beach / park /** ⟨**zoo.**⟩
It is cold and windy.
My grandpa is ² **taking / looking**
a photo of a lion, my grandma
is ³ **playing / talking** to a monkey
and I'm ⁴ **writing / watching** this
postcard!
From Yolanda

3 **Choose a place you like. Write a postcard. Use present continuous verbs.**

We're at _____ It is _____

_____

_____

_____

_____

From _____

5 A naughty monkey!

Lesson One Words

1 Find and circle the animal words. Then write.

monkey

l	h	l	c	a	m	e	l	p	a
i	u	v	m	o	n	k	e	y	j
z	w	k	a	n	g	a	r	o	o
a	f	l	a	m	i	n	g	o	n
r	n	e	p	e	n	g	u	i	n
d	r	u	z	e	b	r	a	m	d
c	r	o	c	o	d	i	l	e	m

2 Write.

That's not a monkey.
It's a zebra.

That's not a monkey.

That's not a monkey.

That's not a monkey.

That's not a monkey.

That's a _____ !

1 **Read and circle the correct answers.** 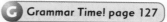 Grammar Time! page 127

1 Is Dad taking a photo?   (Yes, he is.) / No, he isn't.

2 Is the crocodile sleeping?   Yes, it is. / No, it isn't.

3 Is the crocodile swimming?   Yes, it is. / No, it isn't.

4 Are the boys looking at the bird?   Yes, they are. / No, they aren't.

5 Are the boys looking at the crocodile?   Yes, they are. / No, they aren't.

6 Is the girl eating an ice cream?   Yes, she is. / No, she isn't.

2 **Write the questions.**

1 Are you playing computer games?

No, we aren't.

(play computer games)

2

Yes, I am.

(watch TV)

3

No, I'm not.

(listen to music)

4

Yes, we are.

(read comics)

Lesson Three Grammar and Song

1 Look and write. Then answer the questions. **G** Grammar Time! page 127

| wear a hat | write in a notebook | eat a sandwich | take a photo |

Annie   Jo   Liz

1  Annie
Is Annie wearing a hat?
Yes, she is.

2  Jo
_____
_____

3 Liz
_____
_____

4 Jo
_____
_____

5 Annie
_____
_____

6 Liz
_____
_____

2 Read and write the answers.

1 Are the monkeys eating?   No, they aren't.

2 Are the zebras running?   _____

3 Are the tigers playing?   _____

4 Are the parrots talking?   _____

5 Are the penguins walking?   _____

6 Are the parrots flying?   _____

1 **Say the words. Circle the word that doesn't have *or* or *aw*.**

1 horse   corn   (park)   fork   2 farm   paw   yawn   straw

3 fork   scarf   horse   yawn   4 corn   arm   paw   straw

5 horse   corn   car   paw   6 yawn   straw   fork   star

2 **Complete the words.**

1

There's a str__aw__ in the glass.

2

I'm eating with a f____k.

3

They've got a h____se.

4

Look at the dog's p____!

3 **Write.**   horse   fork   ~~straw~~   corn   paw

The dog is holding a [1] _straw_
with its two front [2] _____s.
The [3] _____ is holding a [4] _____
and it's eating [5] _____.

Skills Time!

Reading

1 Order the letters and write the words.

k n i d ___kind___

r s r o y _____

e f r e _____

f n y n u _____

e s a r d c _____

r y g a n _____

2 Read the text in the Class Book. Put the sentences in the correct order.

a The lion is angry. ☐

b A big net falls over the lion. ☐

c "I'm very sorry," says the mouse. ☐

d One year later, the lion is walking in the jungle. ☐

e A mouse runs over the lion's nose and the lion wakes up. ☐

f The mouse hears the lion and it runs to help. ☐

g The mouse makes a big hole and the lion is free. ☐

h A lion is sleeping. 1

i The lion opens its mouth and roars. ☐

Writing

1 Write the speech marks.

1 "Goodbye," says the teacher.

2 I'm taking a photo, says the boy.

3 Open your books, she says. Read the story.

4 The monkeys are my favourite animals, says the girl.

 My writing

2 Read and write the animal names.

1 ___Flamingos___ have got long legs. They are pink and white. They can fly. They can swim and run, too. They live near water.

2 _____ have got arms and legs. They've got hands and fingers, too. They live and sleep in trees. They can climb and jump.

3 Guess the animals. Write about them. Use the correct punctuation.

1 big and tall / brown and red / big feet and big ears / Australia / run and jump

_____

_____

2 big and long / in water / swim and walk / dangerous / eat fish

_____

_____

6 Jim's day

1 Match.

catch the bus ☐

have breakfast [1]

get dressed ☐

brush my hair ☐

walk to school ☐

brush my teeth ☐

get up ☐

have a shower ☐

2 Write.

Every morning, I get up.

Every _____.

1 **Match the questions and answers.**

Harry's day

Molly's day

1 Does Harry get up early?	e	a Yes, she does.
2 Does Molly brush her teeth?	☐	b No, he doesn't.
3 Do Harry and Molly have breakfast?	☐	c No, she doesn't.
4 Does Molly have breakfast with her family?	☐	d No, they don't.
5 Does Harry brush his hair?	☐	e Yes, he does.
6 Do Harry and Molly catch the bus to school?	☐	f Yes, they do.

2 **Write.** **G** Grammar Time! page 128   brush   go   get up   walk   brush   have breakfast

1 (Do you go to school?)   (Yes, I do.)

2 (_____ your hair?)   (No, I don't.)

3 (_____ your teeth?)   (Yes, I do.)

4 (_____ late?)   (No, I don't.)

5 (_____ with your family?)   (Yes, I do.)

6 (_____ to school with your friends?)   (No, I don't.)

Lesson Three Grammar and Song

1 Write about Tom. (G) Grammar Time! page 127 | catch the bus   have breakfast   ~~get up~~

1.
He _doesn't get up_ at quarter past seven.
He _gets up_ at half past seven.

2.
He _____ at eight o'clock.
He _____ at quarter past eight.

3.
He _____ at half past eight.
He _____ at quarter to nine.

2 Read the song in the Class Book. Write, then put the lines in the correct order.

catch   do   have   get up   go   ~~have~~   have   see

My day

a. I _have_ a shower every day. ☐

b. I _____ my school friends every day. ☐

c. Then I _____ outside and play. ☐

d. I _____ my lessons every day. ☐

e. I _____ my homework every day. ☐

f. I _____ my breakfast every day. ☐

g. I _____ early every day. [1]

h. I _____ the school bus every day. ☐

1 Complete the words with *oy* or *oi*.

1 ___oi_l   2 t_____   3 s___l   4 b_____   5 _____ster   6 c___n

2 Write the words.

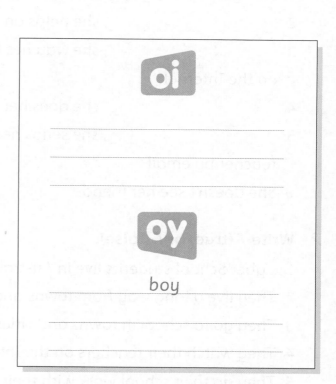

oi
_____
_____
_____
oy
_____ boy
_____
_____

3 Say the words. Circle the word that doesn't have *oy* or *oi*.

1 boy   toy   coin   (stone)   2 oil   coin   coat   soil
3 gate   boy   oyster   oil   4 boy   blue   soil   toy
5 soil   white   coin   oyster   6 oyster   oil   boy   tube

4 Write.   coin   boy   toy

Roy is a ¹_____,
Playing with a ²_____.
He can see a ³_____.

Skills Time!

Lesson Five

Reading

1 Read the text in the Class Book. Write.

> Finally   Next   ~~every day~~   First   Then   at the weekend

1 Ellie gets up early _____ every day _____.

2 _____, she helps on the farm.

3 _____, she watches her teachers on the Internet.

4 _____, she does her school work.

5 _____, she sends her work to her teacher by email.

6 She doesn't see her friends _____.

2 Write _T_ (true) or _F_ (false).

1 Cyber School students live in Australia.   T

2 They live a long way from towns and cities.   ____

3 They go to school in towns and cities.   ____

4 They watch their teachers on the Internet.   ____

5 They do their school work with their friends.   ____

6 They send their work to their teacher by email.   ____

7 They can talk to their friends at school.   ____

8 They meet at the weekend and have a sports day.   ____

Writing

1 Write the sentences. Use capital letters and punctuation marks. Remember the proper nouns.

1 my favourite film is toy story   My favourite film is Toy Story.

2 alice lives in paris

3 mr jones is their teacher

4 max is amy's cousin

 My writing

2 Read and circle the proper nouns.

My family

My name is (Lucy) and I'm nine. There are four people in my family. My brother is called Tim. He is five. My dad is called Steve and my mum is called Jill. We live in a flat near the park.

My favourite things

My favourite day is Thursday because I go swimming every Thursday. My favourite teacher is Miss Wilson. I like lots of films, but my favourite film is Finding Nemo. My favourite month is July because I can play football in the park.

3 Write about the people in your family. Then write about your favourite day, teacher, film and month.

Fluency Time! ②

1 Circle the correct words.

1 Are you good at windsurfing, Dan?   No, I'm **good /** **bad** at windsurfing.

2 Are you good at surfing, Maria?   Yes, I'm very **good / bad** at surfing.

3 Are you good at taking photos, Sue?   No, I'm **good / terrible** at taking photos.

4 Are you good at sailing, Brad?   Yes, I'm quite **bad / good** at sailing.

5 Are you good at football, Jim?   Yes, I'm **good / terrible** at football.

2 Write.

> terrible   quite good   ~~bad~~   very good

1 Are you good at _____ painting _____?

No, I'm not. I'm bad at painting.

2 Are you good at _____?

_____

3 Are you _____?

_____

4 Are _____?

_____

1 **Watch. Who says this? Write *Anna*, *Sam* or *Tom*.**

1 _____Tom_____ He's quite good at running, too. 2 _____ I'm terrible at throwing!

3 _____ Watch this, Anna! 4 _____ Sam's good at basketball.

5 _____ I'm very bad at basketball. 6 _____ It's my turn now.

2 **Complete the descriptions.**

| kicking | a goal | ~~very bad at~~ | good at | terrible at |

This is Anna.
She's [1] _____very bad at_____ basketball.
She's [2] _____ throwing!

This is Sam.
He isn't [3] _____ football,
but he's [4] _____ the ball now.
He's [5] scoring _____.

3 **What are you good at? What are you bad at? Ask and answer.**

Are you good at running?   Yes, I'm quite good at running.

1 Write the verbs.

1 I _____have_____ breakfast.

2 I _____ my homework.

3 I _____ my teeth.

4 I _____ to school.

5 I _____ dressed.

6 I _____ outside.

7 I _____ the bus.

2 Circle the odd one out.

1 kayak   windsurf   dive   (polluted)

2 safe   tall   dolphin   clean

3 sorry   free   kind   water

4 first   ugly   then   next

5 beautiful   waterski   swim   snorkel

6 penguin   monkey   camel   angry

3 Circle the correct words. Then write short answers.

1 Is **he** / **I** diving?   No, _____he isn't_____.

2 Are **I** / **they** surfing?   Yes, _____.

3 Are **she** / **you and Tim** watching the penguins?   No, _____.

4 Does **he** / **they** live in a big house?   Yes, _____.

5 Do **she** / **we** get up early?   No, _____.

6 Does **she** / **you** have a shower in the morning?   Yes, _____.

4 Write.

He _doesn't get_ (get) up at eight o'clock.

They _____ (live) in a big house.

She _____ (have) breakfast with her family.

He _____ (have) a shower in the morning.

They _____ (walk) to school.

She _____ (get) dressed in her bedroom.

My work

My favourite story in Units 4–6 is _____

My favourite song in Units 4–6 is _____

My favourite unit in Units 4–6 is _____

I need to practise _____

My work in Units 4–6 is

 OK   Good   Excellent

Lesson One Words

1 Order the letters and write the words.

   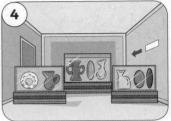

poshping lalm   ncimae   fcéa   smemuu

shopping mall

rarliby   yaplrondgu   snimwigm opol   trossp etcnre

2 Where are the people? Look and write.

1   *They're at the playground.*

2   _____

3   _____

4   _____

1 Look at Jane's diary. Circle *never*, *sometimes* or *always*.

1 She *never* / **sometimes** / **always** goes to the cinema on Wednesdays.

2 She **never** / **sometimes** / **always** goes to the cinema on Tuesdays.

3 She **never** / **sometimes** / **always** goes to the shopping mall on Thursdays.

4 She **never** / **sometimes** / **always** goes to the shopping mall on Tuesdays.

5 She **never** / **sometimes** / **always** goes to the sports centre on Wednesdays.

6 She **never** / **sometimes** / **always** goes to the sports centre on Thursdays.

2 Complete the sentences about Jane with *on*, *at* or *in*.   **G** Grammar Time! page 128

1 She always gets up __at__ eight o'clock.

2 She never goes to school _____ Sundays.

3 She sometimes visits her cousins _____ July.

4 She sometimes goes to bed _____ half past nine.

5 She always has a shower _____ Saturdays.

6 She never wears a coat _____ August.

1 Write. **G** Grammar Time! page 128 | ✓✓ = always   ✓ = sometimes   ✗ = never

 ✓✓

Billy _always plays tennis_.

 ✓

Katie _____

_____ football.

 ✓

Billy _____

_____ basketball.

 ✗

Ben _____

_____ .

 ✗

Jenny _____

_____ .

 ✓✓

Ben _____

_____ .

2 Write true sentences about you. Use *never*, *sometimes* or *always*.

1 _I never get up_ _____ late.

2 _____ my teeth in the morning.

3 _____ breakfast with my family.

4 _____ the bus to school.

5 _____ TV in the evening.

3 Read the song in the Class Book. Tick (✓) the boxes.

Come and play with me!

never	sometimes	always	
	✓		play computer games
			ride my bike
			watch a DVD
			fly my kite
			snorkel in the sea
			read a book
			play my new guitar
			shop
			cook
			surf the Internet
			watch TV
			have a lot of fun

1 **Complete the words with *ow* or *ou*. Are the letters the same (S) or different (D)?**

1 d_ow_n   ___ou t   D

2 br___n   fl___er   _____

3 sh___t   cl___n   _____

4 m___se   tr___sers   _____

5 c___   h___se   _____

2 **Write.**

house   trousers   brown   mouse   flowers   ~~clown~~

The ¹___clown___ 's got ²_____,
Red and blue.
He's wearing ³_____ ⁴_____,
But only one shoe.
He's sitting in his ⁵_____,
He looks behind a wall.
He's scared of a ⁶_____,
But it's only small.

3 **Write.**

1 The boy's wearing a T-shirt and ____trousers____ .

2 Please come to my _____.

3 The _____ is wearing a hat.

4 This is a beautiful _____.

5 A _____ is bigger than a monkey.

6 A _____ is smaller than a horse.

Reading

1 **Look and write. Find the secret word (↓).**

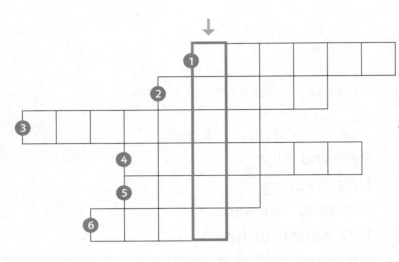

What's the secret word? _____

2 **Read the Class Book. Order the lines and write the numbers.**

a When Mike is a teenager, he goes to Monsters University. ☐

b Now the two monsters are friends. ☐

c Mike and Sulley go to the human world and they can't get back. ☐

d He meets Sulley at Monsters University, but they are not friends at first. ☐

e One day, Mike visits Monsters Inc. ☐ 1

f They get jobs at Monsters Inc. and they have fun working together! ☐

g Mike and Sulley get home to the monster world. ☐

h Mike wants to be a scary monster when he grows up. ☐

i They work together to escape from the human world. ☐

3 **Write _T_ (true) or _F_ (false).**

1 In _Monsters University_ there are two worlds.   _T_

2 The monsters want to be funny.   _____

3 Sulley and Mike want to live with humans.   _____

4 The monsters can sing really well.   _____

Writing

1 Read and complete the table.

		verb	adjective	preposition
1	Ellie lives on a big farm.	lives		
2	I watch old films on TV.			
3	They're sailing in a little boat.			
4	My new friend often goes to concerts.			

 My writing

2 Read and write the names.

Dear Ian,
Do you like the theatre?
Do you want to go on Saturday?
From Mark

Hello Sam,
Do you like music? There's a
concert at the theatre on Monday.
Do you want to go?
Bye. Katya

Dear ¹_____,
I can't go to the theatre on Saturday.
I always visit my family at the
weekend. Let's go another day.
From ²_____

Dear ³_____,
I go to the sports centre on
Mondays. I can't go to the concert
with you.
From ⁴_____

3 You are going to the cinema.

Write an invitation. Use these words.

like	want	go	on

8 I'd like a melon!

Lesson One Words

1 Write.

pasta and

meat

bread and

_____

meat and

_____

cereal and

_____

a melon and a

_____

an onion and a

_____

a lemon and an

_____

a cucumber and a

_____

2 Look and write a shopping list.

She'd like a _____ cucumber _____ .

She'd like a _____ .

She'd like a _____ .

She'd like an _____ .

She'd like some _____ .

She'd like some _____ .

She'd like some _____ .

She'd like some _____ .

1 **Write.** **G** Grammar Time! page 129

pasta   bread   apple   egg   biscuits   rice   orange   fries

1 _He'd like some pasta._   2 _____

3 _____   4 _____

5 _____   6 _____

7 _____   8 _____

2 **Complete the questions and write the answers.**

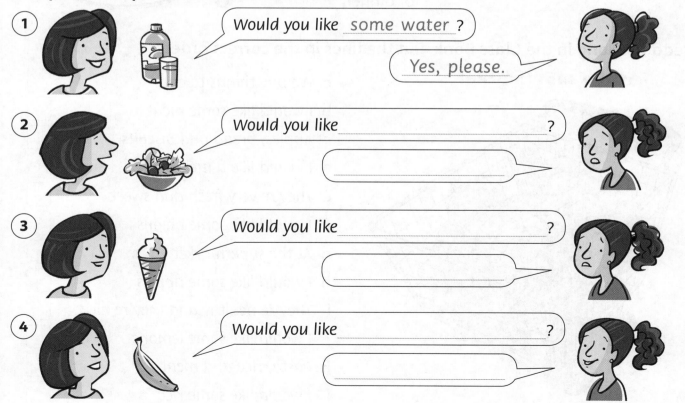

1 Would you like _some water_ ?

   Yes, please.

2 Would you like _____ ?

   _____

3 Would you like _____ ?

   _____

4 Would you like _____ ?

   _____

Would you like a banana?   No, thanks.   **Unit 8**   **59**

1 Complete the questions with *a* or *some* and a food word. Grammar Time! page 129

1 Would you like some onions , Stacy? — Yes, please.

2 Would you like _____? — No, thanks.

3 Would you like _____, Ollie? — Yes, please.

4 Would you like _____? — No, thanks.

5 Would you like _____, Emma? — Yes, please.

6 Would you like _____? — No, thanks.

2 What would you like for dinner? Write *a*, *an* or *some* and food words.

I'd like _____

_____

_____ for dinner.

3 Read the song in the Class Book. Put the lines in the correct order.

At the supermarket

a We buy things to eat

b I would like some meat

c Apples, bread and biscuits

d I would like a melon

e They're very fresh and sweet

f I would like some onions   9

g At the supermarket

h I would like some apples

i They're healthy and they're nice

j I would like some lemons

k Pasta, rice and meat

l I would like some rice

1 **Say the words with *ld* and *lt*. Circle the odd one out. Write this word.**

| adult | field | child | ~~quilt~~ |

1 _____quilt_____

2 _____

3 _____

4 _____

2 **Complete the words. Write *T* (true) or *F* (false).** | ld | lt |

1 There's a chi**ld**____ in the bedroom.   ___T___

2 There's a be_____ on the chair.   _____

3 There's a qui____ on the bed.   _____

4 There's a shie_____ on the door.   _____

5 There are some cows in the fie____.   _____

6 There's an adu_____ in the bedroom.   _____

3 **Write.** | field   quilt   ~~adult~~   shield |

A child and an [1] _____adult_____

Are standing in a [2] _____.

The adult's got a [3] _____.

The child's got a [4] _____.

Skills Time!

Reading

1 Circle the words and write.

s a l t (p e a s) c h e e s e p o t a t o p e p p e r b u t t e r

1 _____peas_____
2 _____
3 _____
4 _____
5 _____
6 _____

2 Read the text in the Class Book. Write a shopping list for *My Favourite Dish*.

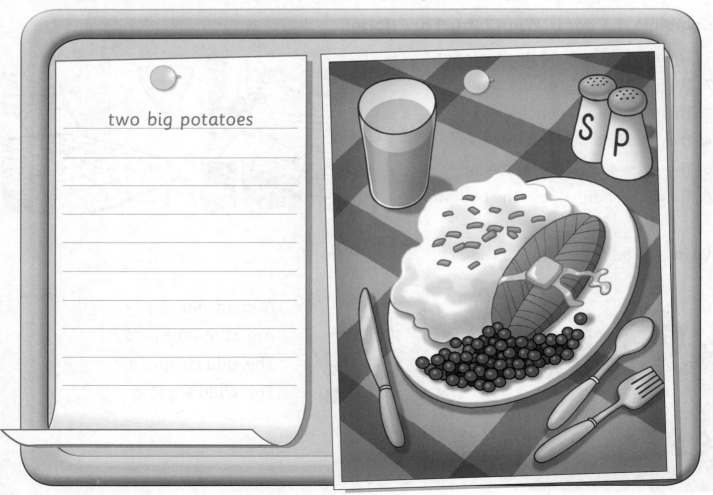

two big potatoes

Writing

1 **Order the words and write.**

1 He's playing with a ___small___ , ___blue___ ___ball___ . | small ball blue

2 She's wearing _____ , _____ . | pink big sunglasses

3 You need a _____ , _____ . | red onion big

4 He's sailing in a _____ , _____ . | boat little red

5 We'd like a _____ , _____ . | green cucumber long

2 **Complete the instructions.** | butter   bread   grapes   cheese

How to make my favourite sandwich

You take some ¹ ___bread___ .

You put some ² _____ on the bread.

You take some ³ _____ and you

put it on the bread.

Then you take some ⁴ _____ and

you put them on top.

This is my favourite sandwich. It's great!

3 **Write instructions for making your favourite sandwich.**

You take _____

You put _____

_____

_____

_____

The fastest animal in the world

1 Look and count. Write the numbers.

1 There are ___four___ lakes.

2 There are _____ mountains.

3 There are _____ waterfalls.

4 There are _____ oceans.

2 Write.

| wide | waterfall | ocean | big | deep | mountain | lake | high |

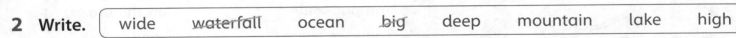

This is a ___big waterfall___ .

This is a _____ .

This is a _____ .

This is a _____ .

1 Read and tick (✓) or cross (✗) each sentence. ⒢ Grammar Time! page 129

1 Ben's taller than Carl. ✓
2 Carl's taller than Adam. ✗
3 Adam's the tallest. ☐

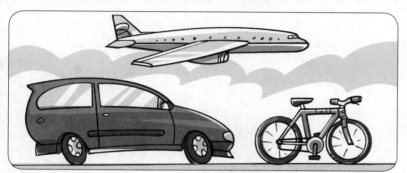

4 Planes are the fastest. ☐
5 Bikes are faster than cars. ☐
6 Cars are faster than bikes. ☐

7 Cheetahs are the biggest. ☐
8 Cheetahs are bigger than mice. ☐
9 Elephants are the biggest. ☐

2 Write.

1 Carl is the _____shortest_____. (short)
2 Ben is _____ than Adam. (short)
3 Bikes are the _____. (slow)
4 Cars are _____ than planes. (slow)
5 Cheetahs are _____ than elephants. (small)
6 Mice are the _____. (small)

3 Write the answers.

1 Are cheetahs faster than elephants? _Yes, they are._
2 Are bikes bigger than cars? _____
3 Is Ben the tallest boy? _____

My sandcastle is the biggest! **Unit 9** 65

1 Look at the table. Circle the mistake in each sentence.
Write the correct sentence. **G** Grammar Time! page 129

smallest	the UK	Australia	Russia	biggest
shortest	hen	horse	giraffe	tallest
slowest	car	train	plane	fastest

1 A train is (faster) than a plane.

    A train is slower than a plane.

2 A hen is taller than a horse.

3 Australia is smaller than the UK.

4 A plane is slower than a car.

5 The UK is bigger than Russia.

6 A giraffe is shorter than a horse.

2 Tick (✓) the correct answer.

1 Which transport is faster?   a plane ✓   a car ☐

2 Which country is smaller?   the UK ☐   Russia ☐

3 What's the tallest animal?   a giraffe ☐   a hen ☐   a cow ☐

4 What's the slowest transport?   a train ☐   a plane ☐   a car ☐

5 What's the biggest country?   Russia ☐   Australia ☐   the USA ☐

6 What's the shortest animal?   a hen ☐   a horse ☐   a sheep ☐

1 Say the words with *nd*, *nt* and *mp*. Circle the odd one out. Write this word.

1  ____sand____

2 _____

3 _____

4 _____

2 Complete the words.

nd   nt   mp

1 There's a frog in the po__nd__.
2 She's playing in the sa____.
3 I like sleeping in a te____.
4 He's holding a la____.
5 There's a ca____ in the field.
6 There's a pla____ under the tree.

3 Write.   aunt   camp   lamp   wind   pond   ~~tent~~   plant

We put up the ¹ ___tent___
At the big, big ² _____.
We hear the ³ _____.
We light the ⁴ _____.
We sit by the ⁵ _____.
We look at the ⁶ _____s.
We're happy together,
Just me and my ⁷ _____.

Skills Time!

Reading

1 Order the letters and write the words.

d l o

old

e i b d r g

_____

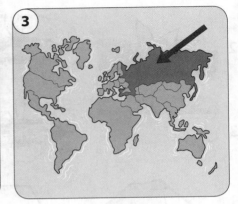

y c t r n o u

_____

r v e r i

_____

l g n o

_____

i n b l d i g u

_____

2 Read the text in the Class Book and write.

1 The Ggantija temples are the ___oldest temples___ in Europe. They are over _____ years old.

2 The two bridges over Lake Pontchartrain are the _____ over water in the world. They are nearly _____ miles long.

3 Russia is the _____ in the world. It is about _____ square kilometres.

4 The Nile is the _____ in the world. It is _____ kilometres long.

Writing

1   Circle all the words you can use.

1   … she watches TV in the evening.   Always / Sometimes / Never

2   He … plays computer games at night.   always / sometimes / never

3   He has a shower in the morning …   always / sometimes / never

4   He … goes to the theatre on Saturdays.   always / sometimes / never

5   … they play football after school.   Always / Sometimes / Never

6   We … go swimming at the beach.   always / sometimes / never

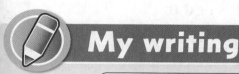

My writing

2   Write.

| make | holiday | mall | Saturdays |
| living | tomato | tennis | rivers |

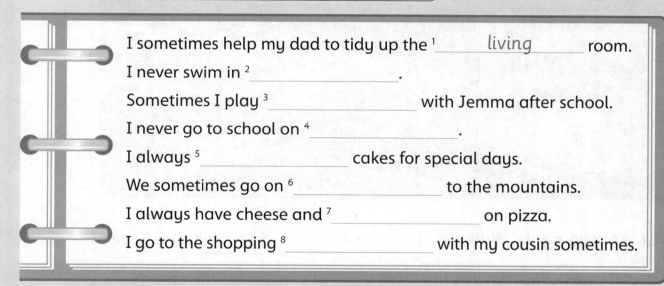

I sometimes help my dad to tidy up the ¹ _____living_____ room.

I never swim in ² _____.

Sometimes I play ³ _____ with Jemma after school.

I never go to school on ⁴ _____.

I always ⁵ _____ cakes for special days.

We sometimes go on ⁶ _____ to the mountains.

I always have cheese and ⁷ _____ on pizza.

I go to the shopping ⁸ _____ with my cousin sometimes.

3   Write sentences about you. Use _always_, _sometimes_ and _never_.

_____

_____

_____

_____

_____

Everyday English

1 Look at the map. Write.
café   ~~library~~   shopping mall   swimming pool

1 Excuse me. Where's the library ?
It's next to the theatre.

2 Can you tell me the way to the
_____ ?
Sure. Go straight on.
It's next to the playground.

3 Excuse me. Where's the
_____ ?
Turn right, then go straight on.
You can't miss it.

4 Can you tell me the way to the
_____ ?
Sure. Turn left. It's next to
the supermarket.

2 Look at the map again. Write.
left   ~~next to~~   go straight on   right

1 Excuse me. Where's the
sports centre?
It's next to the cinema.

2 Can you tell me the way to
the museum?
Sure. Turn _____ .
It's opposite the supermarket.

3 Excuse me. Where's the park?
Turn _____ , then
go straight on.

4 Can you tell me the way to
the cinema?
Sure. _____ .
You can't miss it.

1 Watch. Read the directions and write the places.

cinema   museum   post office

1 (Turn left at the post office.) _____

2 (Turn right. Then go straight on.) _____

3 (It's next to the museum.) _____

2 Read and circle. Then match.

1 Excuse me. Where's the
   bank / cinema / museum?

a

2 Sure. Turn left at the
   cinema / post office / museum.

b

3 Can you **show / tell / say /**
   me the way to the
   library, please?

c

4 Turn **left / right / straight**, then
   go straight on.

d

3 Think about your town. You are at the school door. Ask and answer.

Where's the …?   It's next to   Go straight on   Turn left   Turn right

(Can you tell me the way to the museum, please?)   (Sure. Turn right …)

1 Find and circle the words. Write the words with *a*, *an* and *some*.

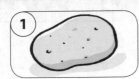

a potato

a	r	a	e	p	b	n	s	m
e	o	c	e	a	n	u	i	r
b	b	u	i	l	d	i	n	g
p	c	c	a	r	b	g	b
o	e	u	e	k	i	u	e	r
t	n	m	r	e	i	t	r	i
a	g	b	e	c	i	t	y	d
t	h	e	a	t	r	e	u	g
o	b	r	l	i	i	r	c	e
o	n	i	o	n	n	b	o	i

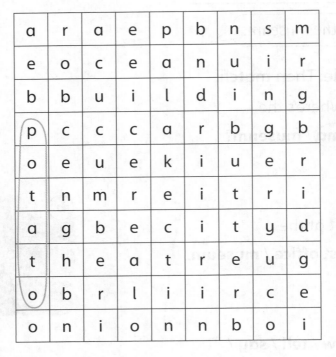

2 Write.

wide	big	deep	~~old~~	long

The swimming pool in my town is 50 years [1] _____old_____ . The pool is 30 metres [2] _____

and 10 metres [3] _____ . The water is 1 metre [4] _____ . It is quite [5] _____ .

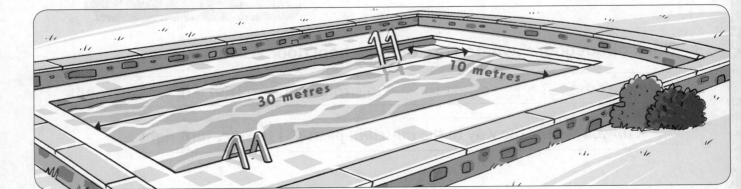

30 metres

10 metres

3 **Complete the words. Then write the answers.**

1 Are the pyramids old _er_ than Big Ben?   Yes, they are.

2 Is Brazil big_____ than Russia?   _____

3 Is the cheetah the fast_____ animal in the world?   _____

4 Are the Pontchartrain bridges the short_____ in the world?   _____

4 **Write s if you need to. Look and answer Yes, please or No, thanks.**

1 ◁ Would you like some water ___ ?   No, thanks.

2 ◁ Would you like some pea_s_ ?   _____

3 ◁ Would you like some cheese ___ ?   _____

4 ◁ Would you like some apple ___ ?   _____

5 ◁ Would you like some pasta ___ ?   _____

My work

My favourite story in Units 7–9 is _____

My favourite song in Units 7–9 is _____

My favourite unit in Units 7–9 is _____

I need to practise _____

My work in Units 7–9 is

 OK   **Good**   **Excellent**

10 In the park!

1 Complete the crossword.

Down ↓   Across →

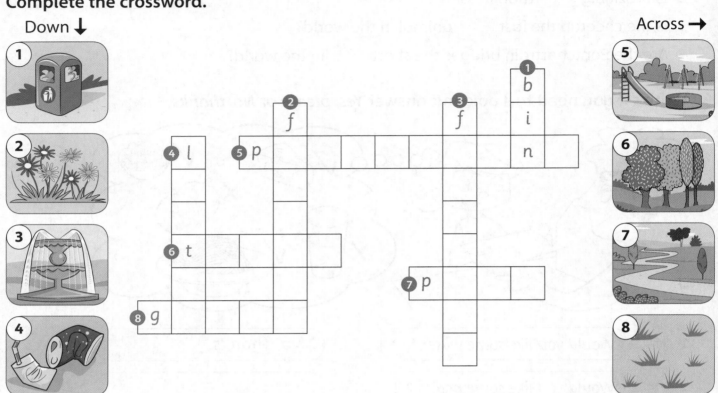

2 Write.

1 There's a rabbit on the ___grass___ .

2 There's some _____ under the slide.

3 There's a dog in the _____ .

4 There are some children in the _____ .

5 There are some _____ near the wall.

6 There's a cat on the _____ .

1 **Look at the signs. Write *must* or *mustn't*.**  Grammar Time! page 130

1 You ___mustn't___ play in the fountain.
2 You _____ walk your dog here.
3 You _____ put litter in the bin.
4 You _____ walk on the grass.
5 You _____ pick the flowers.

2 **Complete the sentences with *must* or *mustn't*.** be   do   pick   ~~swim~~

1 You ___mustn't swim___ here. The water is very deep.

2 You _____ quiet. Grandma is sleeping.

3 You _____ your homework. Then you can play outside.

4 You _____ the flowers. They aren't your flowers.

1 Look at the signs. Write sentences with *must* or *mustn't*.  Grammar Time! page 130

1 wash / hands
 You must wash your hands.

2 walk / dog

3 put / litter / bin

4 walk / grass

5 turn / off / mobile phone

2 Complete the song with *must* or *mustn't*.

You must come to the park

Oh, you ¹_____must_____ come to the park,
So we can have some fun.
You ²_____ come to the park today,
And play games in the sun.
Oh, we ³_____ walk on the path,
And we ⁴_____ climb the trees.
We ⁵_____ put litter in the bin,
Let's keep the park clean, please.
Oh, we ⁶_____ be very good,
And we ⁷_____ pick the flowers.
But we can have a lot of fun,
And play for hours and hours.

1 Complete the words with *ai*, *ay* or *a_e*.

| 1 | 2 | 3 | 4 | 5 | 6 |

r _ai_ n   Mond____   r__c__   tr____n   tr_____   c__s__

2 Write.

race   train   today   rain   case   ~~Monday~~   play

It's ¹ ____Monday____ ² _____,
And I can ³ _____.
Outside there's ⁴ _____,
But I'm in with my ⁵ _____s.
I open my ⁶ _____,
And the trains have a ⁷ _____!

3 Circle the correct spelling.

1. trai
   (tray)

2. rayc
   race

3. trane
   train

4. Mondai
   Monday

5. cais
   case

6. rain
   rayn

Reading

1 Look and write. Find the extra word (↓) and answer the question.

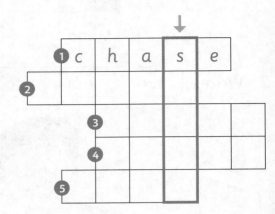

	↓	
① c	h	a	s	e
②				
③				
④				
⑤				

What word is the same as 'talk loudly'? _____

2 Read the text in the Class Book. Put the sentences in the correct order.

a The old woman wants to eat the Gingerbread Man. ☐

b The Gingerbread Man runs away. ☐

c The old woman chases him. ☐

d An old woman makes a Gingerbread Man. 1

e He wants to cross the river, but he can't swim. ☐

f The Gingerbread Man meets a cat. ☐

g The Gingerbread Man runs to the river. ☐

h The cat wants to eat the Gingerbread Man. ☐

i The Gingerbread Man sits on the fox's nose. ☐

j The fox opens its mouth and eats the Gingerbread Man. ☐

k There is a fox near the river. ☐

l The Gingerbread Man sits on the fox's head and the fox starts to swim. ☐

Writing

1 Write *and* or *or*.

1 She doesn't like maths _____or_____ English.

2 He plays football _____ tennis.

3 I don't live in a town _____ a city.

4 We like maths _____ science.

5 I like eating bread _____ jam.

6 They don't play basketball _____ volleyball.

 My writing

2 Write. Tick (✓) the rules that are the same in your school.

~~teacher~~   comics   MP3 player   quiet   homework

School rules

You must listen to the ¹ _____teacher_____ and work hard. ☐

You mustn't read ² _____ or eat in the classroom. ☐

You must do your ³ _____ and turn off your mobile phone. ☐

You mustn't listen to your ⁴ _____ or CD player. ☐

You must be ⁵ _____ and be kind to other children. ☐

3 Write a poster for your school rules. Use *and* and *or*.

School rules

_____

_____

_____

_____

_____

Lesson One Words

1 Look and count. Write the numbers.

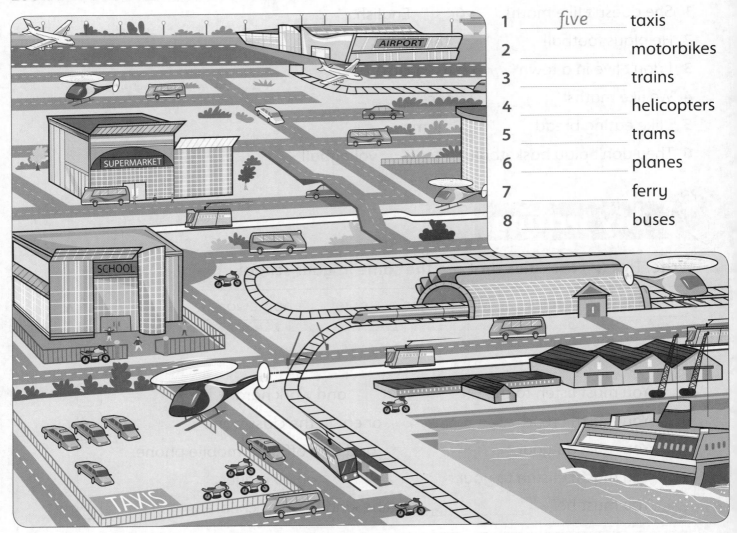

1 _five_ taxis
2 _____ motorbikes
3 _____ trains
4 _____ helicopters
5 _____ trams
6 _____ planes
7 _____ ferry
8 _____ buses

2 Write T (true) or F (false).

1 There's a tram under the bridge.   F

2 There's a train at the station.   ___

3 There's a bus in front of the supermarket.   ___

4 There's a ferry at the airport.   ___

5 There's a bus on the bridge.   ___

6 There's a taxi in front of the supermarket.   ___

7 There's a plane at the airport.   ___

8 There's a motorbike in front of the school.

1 Write *There was* or *There were*.  Grammar Time! page 130

1 <u>There was</u> a hotel in our town a hundred years ago.

2 _____ trams in our town a hundred years ago.

3 _____ some buses in our town a hundred years ago.

4 _____ a park in our town a hundred years ago.

5 _____ lots of bikes in our town a hundred years ago.

6 _____ a museum in our town a hundred years ago.

2 Write *There was, There were, There wasn't* or *There weren't*.

seven o'clock

ten o'clock

1 <u>There weren't</u> any books at seven o'clock.

2 _____ some flowers at seven o'clock.

3 _____ a camera at seven o'clock.

4 _____ a computer at seven o'clock.

5 _____ a banana at seven o'clock.

6 _____ any pens at seven o'clock.

7 _____ a camera at ten o'clock.

8 _____ some flowers at ten o'clock.

There were lots of kangaroos. Unit 11 **81**

1 Circle the correct words. 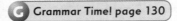 Grammar Time! page 130

200 years ago

50 years ago

1 There weren't any cars **fifty years ago** / (**two hundred years ago**.)

2 There were motorbikes **fifty years ago** / **two hundred years ago**.

3 There weren't any bikes **fifty years ago** / **two hundred years ago**.

4 There weren't any buses **fifty years ago** / **two hundred years ago**.

5 There were taxis **fifty years ago** / **two hundred years ago**.

6 There were planes **fifty years ago** / **two hundred years ago**.

2 Read the song in the Class Book. Write about the town two hundred years ago.

Our town has a history

1 _There weren't any_ buses.

2 _____ and markets.

3 _____ planes.

4 _____ and theatres.

5 _____ trains.

1 **Look at the words with _ea_, _ee_ and _y_. Circle the odd one out.**

Then write these words with the correct pictures.

1 green   week   (dream)   2 lolly   queen   family

3 please   seat   happy   4 jelly   tree   sheep

5 family   ice cream   funny

 **a** 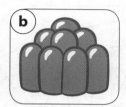 **b**  **c**  **d**  **e**

_____   _____   _____   _____   __dream__

2 **Write.** | queen   happy   green   ~~dream~~   jelly   ice cream |

In my ¹_____dream_____,

I am a ²_____.

I eat ³_____ ⁴_____,

With ⁵_____.

I'm very ⁶_____,

In my dream.

3 **Write.**

 **1**  **2**  **3**  **4**  **5**

1 My mum is sitting under a _____tree_____.

2 There are five people in my _____.

3 Can you get me a melon, _____?

4 He's eating a _____.

5 There's a _____ on the path.

Skills Time!

Reading

1 Look and write.

| along | through | in the middle of | at the top of | between | inside |

1 A girl is going _____through_____ the gate.

2 A boy is walking _____ the path.

3 A girl is _____ the play house.

4 A girl is _____ the playground.

5 A girl is _____ the slide.

6 A boy is _____ the seesaw and the slide.

2 Read the Class Book. Write *T* (true) or *F* (false).

1 Petra is in the middle of a forest.   F

2 Petra was a capital city.

3 The buildings in Petra were small.

4 There weren't any people in Petra for hundreds of years.

5 In 1989, Petra was in a film.

6 Petra is now famous all over the world.

Writing

1 **Read. How many topics are there?**

Match the topics with the paragraphs.

transport   food   money

There were fruit trees in Petra and there was a lot of fruit to eat. The city was in the desert, but it had a lot of water. There were special ways to bring water to the city.

_____

There were shops and markets in Petra. There were coins to buy things, too. The heads of kings were on the coins. _____

The Nabatean people were travellers. There weren't any buses or trains, but they had camels.

_____

My writing

2 **Write.**   is   isn't   was   ~~wasn't~~   are   aren't   were   weren't

Fifty years ago, there ¹ __wasn't__ a shopping mall in my town. There ² _____
only one café. There was a museum then. There ³ _____ any buses, but there
⁴ _____ trams.

Now, there ⁵ _____ lots of cafés. There ⁶ _____ a shopping mall, but there
⁷ _____ a museum. There are buses now, but there ⁸ _____ any trams.

3 **Write two paragraphs about your town fifty years ago and now.**

Fifty years ago, _____

_____

_____

Now, _____

_____

_____

Lesson One Words

1 Order the letters and write the words.

altl

tall

dol

_____

hsy

_____

ypttre

_____

gnuyo

_____

htsro

_____

saohdnme

_____

ydfiernl

_____

2 Choose from the words above. Write.

He's _____ _shy_ _____.

He's _____.

He's _____.

He's _____.

She's _____.

She's _____.

She's _____.

She's _____.

1 **Read and tick (✓) the correct sentence.**  Grammar Time! page 131

Last Saturday ...

1 The children were at the beach. ☐
   The children weren't at the beach. ✓

2 It was hot. ☐
   It wasn't hot. ☐

3 Mum was hungry. ☐
   Mum wasn't hungry. ☐

4 The children were sad. ☐
   The children weren't sad. ☐

5 It was windy. ☐
   It wasn't windy. ☐

6 Dad was wet. ☐
   Dad wasn't wet. ☐

2 **Complete the sentences with *He had* or *He didn't have*.** 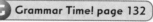 Grammar Time! page 132

Yesterday ...

1 _He didn't have_ _____ breakfast in the living room.

2 _____ cereal for breakfast.

3 _____ a music lesson.

4 _____ sandwiches and an apple for lunch.

5 _____ dinner with his family.

6 _____ rice for dinner.

1 **Look and circle the correct words.**

When he was two years old, …

1 he was **shy** / **friendly**.

2 he had **long hair** / **short hair**.

3 he was **short** / **tall**.

4 he was **young** / **old**.

2 **Write true sentences about you. Use *was*, *wasn't*, *had* or *didn't have*.**

When I was four years old, …

I _____ shy.

I _____ short.

I _____ long hair.

When I was six years old, …

I _____ friendly.

I _____ short hair.

I _____ tall.

3 **Complete the song with *was* or *had*.**

When my grandpa was a boy

When my grandpa ¹ ___was___ a boy,

He ² _____ a lot like me.

He ³ _____ a house and garden,

And a happy family.

Grandpa ⁴ _____ a happy boy,

And he ⁵ _____ lots of friends.

They ⁶ _____ lessons every day,

And they ⁷ _____ fun at weekends.

When my grandpa ⁸ _____ a boy,

He ⁹ _____ fun every day.

He ¹⁰ _____ lots of books to read,

And lots of games to play.

1 **Say the words. Circle the word that doesn't have a long vowel sound *i*.**

1 sky   night   (six)   smile   2 bin   shine   dry   light

3 smile   tin   sky   dry   4 night   fig   shine   light

5 sky   night   fish   shine   6 dry   light   smile   pink

2 **Write.** | shine   light   ~~dry~~   smile   night   white   sky |

In the ¹ ___dry___ , ² _____ ³ _____
There's a ⁴ _____ so ⁵ _____ .
It makes me ⁶ _____
As it ⁷ _____ s all night.

3 **Write.**

1 We ____smile____ when we're happy.   2 Please wash and _____ your hands.

3 Some animals don't sleep at _____ .   4 There's a plane in the _____ .

5 We can't see when there isn't   6 Sometimes the sun doesn't

any _____ .   _____ .

Skills Time!

Reading

1 Write.

| relaxed | mean | ~~miserable~~ | generous | cheerful | worried |

She's ___miserable___,
but he's _____.

He's _____,
but she's _____.

He's _____,
but she's _____.

2 Read the text in the Class Book. Write T (true) or F (false).

1 When Grandma was ten, her eyes were green.   ___F___

2 When Grandma was ten, she had short, brown hair.   _____

3 When Grandma was ten, she was pretty.   _____

4 When Grandma was twenty-two, she had her wedding day.   _____

5 When Grandma was twenty-two, she was very pretty.   _____

6 When Grandma was twenty-two, she had a baby girl.   _____

7 Now Grandma's hair is long and white.   _____

8 Now Grandma's very miserable all the time.   _____

9 Now Grandma's always nice and generous.   _____

Writing

1 Write *and* or *but*.

1 My uncle is old, _____but_____ he's handsome.

2 My aunt is generous _____ she's relaxed.

3 My brother is mean, _____ he's cheerful.

4 My mum is pretty, _____ she isn't tall.

My writing

2 Choose *and* or *but* each time.

This is a photo of my grandma and grandpa. My grandpa is 65 now ¹ **(and)** / **but** he's got white hair. In the photo, he was 25 ² **and** / **but** he had black hair. He was friendly, ³ **and** / **but** he wasn't handsome. My grandma is 63 now. She's got short hair. When she was 23, she had long hair. She was cheerful ⁴ **and** / **but** pretty.

3 Find a photo of your family. Write about the people. Use *and* and *but*.

| This is a photo of … My … is …'s got … In the photo, … He / She |

_____

_____

_____

_____   Put your photo here.

_____

_____

_____

_____

Everyday English

1 **Read and tick (✓).**

① She looks cheerful. ☐
She looks miserable. ✓

② I think he's shy. ☐
I think he's friendly. ☐

③ He's always generous. ☐
He's always mean. ☐

④ She looks clever. ☐
She looks relaxed. ☐

2 **Write.**

class   very   do   looks   know
miserable   think   too   generous

1

Do you know Greg?

Yes, I __do__ . He's in my class.

What's he like? He looks _____ .

No, I think he is always cheerful.

Is he interesting, _____ ?

Yes, he is. He's very interesting.

2

Do you _____ Katya?

Yes, I do. She's in my _____ .

What's she like? She _____ kind.

Yes, I _____ she is kind.

Is she _____ , too?

Yes, she's _____ generous.

1 Watch. Order the words. Then match.

1 her / know / you / Do

  Do you know her?

2 lives / I / in / street / know / she / that / my

  _____

3 my / class / school / in / She's / at

  _____

4 is / think / she / I / friendly

  _____

a

b 1

c

d

2 Watch again. Order the dialogue.

She's in my class at school. ☐

Do you know her? ☐

I think she is friendly. ☐

Look! That's Sara. 1

What's Sara like? ☐

I know that she lives in my street. ☐

She always smiles and says hello. ☐

She looks friendly. ☐

3 Ask and answer about your friends.

What's Kim like?   I think she's generous.

Review 4

1 Choose the correct word. Then write.

old   sorry   ~~handsome~~   relaxed

My grandpa was _____handsome_____ .

The boy is _____ .

My dad is _____ .

My grandma is _____ .

2 Join the words and make sentences.

1 The boys are walking   in the middle of   the taxi.

2 The man is   along   the grass.

3 The flowers are   on top of   the bus and the train.

4 The bike is   between   the tree.

5 The bird is   inside   the path.

3 Write *must* or *mustn't*. Tick (✓) or cross (✗) the rules that are the same in your family.

1 You _____must_____ brush your teeth every day.   ✓

2 You _____ eat in bed. _____

3 You _____ shout at your mum and dad. _____

4 You _____ help your mum and dad. _____

5 You _____ play football in the house. _____

6 You _____ be very good. _____

4 Write *T* (true) or *F* (false).

50 years ago

1 There was a bridge. ___F___

2 There were flowers. _____

3 There were swings. _____

4 There was a river. _____

5 There were bins. _____

6 There was a café. _____

5 Write *There was*, *There were*, *There wasn't* or *There weren't*.

1 _There wasn't_ a bridge.

2 _____ a fountain.

3 _____ trees.

4 _____ a playground.

5 _____ birds.

6 _____ paths.

My work

My favourite story in Units 10–12 is _____

My favourite song in Units 10–12 is _____

My favourite unit in Units 10–12 is _____

I need to practise _____

My work in Units 10–12 is

 OK   Good   Excellent

13

The Ancient Egyptians

Lesson One Words

1 Find and circle the verbs. Then write.

_____use_____

_____

o	p	q	x	w	d	m	n
w	h	e	y	a	f	a	d
u	a	w	v	n	i	l	m
s	t	a	r	t	n	o	k
e	e	b	i	l	i	v	e
c	b	j	m	k	s	e	p
x	t	z	b	a	h	f	t
o	l	a	u	g	h	u	r

_____

_____

_____

_____

_____

_____

2 Write. Choose from the words above.

1 They _____start_____ school at half past eight in the morning.

2 They _____ a computer to write emails.

3 They _____ in an old house.

4 They _____ kayaking. It's their favourite sport.

5 They _____ school at three o'clock in the afternoon.

6 They _____ getting up early in winter. It's very cold.

7 They _____ something to eat. They're hungry.

8 They _____ when they read a funny story.

1 **Circle the correct words.**

1 He hated his dinner on **Saturday** / **Sunday**.

2 He finished his homework on **Saturday** / **Sunday**.

3 He started reading a book on **Saturday** / **Sunday**.

4 He used the computer on **Saturday** / **Sunday**.

5 He loved his dinner on **Saturday** / **Sunday**.

6 He laughed at a TV programme on **Saturday** / **Sunday**.

2 **Complete the sentences.** 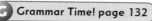 Grammar Time! page 132

They _worked_ (work) in the garden yesterday.

They _didn't play_ (play) computer games.

He _____ (listen) to music yesterday.

He _____ (watch) TV.

She _____ (watch) a play yesterday.

She _____ (cook) a fish pie.

They _____ (play) basketball yesterday.

They _____ (watch) a puppet show.

1 **Write in the past simple. Then tick (✓) the sentences that are true for you.**

G Grammar Time! page 132

| play | listen | play | watch | play | watch |

1 I ____played____ football at the weekend. ☐

2 I _____ TV at the weekend. ☐

3 I _____ computer games at the weekend. ☐

4 I _____ to music at the weekend. ☐

5 I _____ the guitar at the weekend. ☐

6 I _____ a DVD at the weekend. ☐

2 **Write things you did and didn't do at the weekend.**

1 I _____ at the weekend.

2 I _____ at the weekend.

3 I didn't _____ at the weekend.

4 I didn't _____ at the weekend.

3 **Read the song in the Class Book. Complete the table.**

Things I did on my birthday	Things I didn't do on my birthday
I opened _lots of birthday cards._	I didn't _____
I started _____	I didn't _____
Lots of _____	
We _____	
I _____	
We _____	

1 **Say the words with *ow*, *oa* and *o_e*. Circle the odd one out. Write this word.**

nose   soap   snow   elbow

1 _____ soap _____

2 _____

3 _____

4 _____

2 Write.   nose   coat   elbow   snow

I put on my ¹ _____ coat _____
And go out in the ² _____ .
There is snow on my ³ _____
And on my ⁴ _____ .

3 Write.

1 I wash my hands with _____ soap _____ and water.

2 In winter, I put on my warm _____ .

3 I've got brown eyes and a small _____ .

4 My _____ is on my arm.

5 A _____ is hard.

6 There is a lot of _____ in Russia in winter.

Skills Time!

Reading

1 Circle the correct words.

1 Clay tablets were very **heavy** / **light**.

2 They were very **hard** / **soft** when they were dry.

3 Clay tablets were **difficult** / **easy** to break.

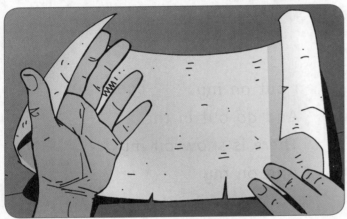

4 Papyrus was very **light** / **heavy**.

5 It was also **hard** / **soft**.

6 Papyrus was **easy** / **difficult** to make.

2 Read the Class Book. Write *T* (true) or *F* (false).

1 Five thousand years ago, people wrote on paper.   F

2 People used a reed to write on wet clay.   _____

3 Clay tablets were very heavy.   _____

4 They were difficult to break.   _____

5 People used each tablet many times.   _____

6 Papyrus is a kind of plant.   _____

7 Papyrus was soft and light.   _____

8 People in other countries also started to use papyrus.   _____

9 Papyrus was not expensive.   _____

10 Sometimes people washed papyrus and used it again.   _____

Writing

1 **Draw * at the start of each new paragraph.**

* The Ancient Egyptians had brown eyes and black hair.   Men and women had long hair.
They were not very tall, but they were healthy.   There weren't any roads in Ancient Egypt.
People walked or travelled by boat on the River Nile.   People used donkeys to carry things
on land.   The Ancient Egyptians didn't have shops and they didn't use money.   There was
a market in town.   They exchanged food and drink and other things.

My writing

2 **Write.**   playing   write   helped   balls   had   school

doll

leather ball

wooden animal

Ancient Egyptian children loved ¹ ____playing____ with wooden animals.
They ² _____ dolls and they also played with ³ _____ .
Only boys from rich families studied at ⁴ _____ . They learned to read and
⁵ _____ . They studied maths and languages, too. Girls stayed at home and
⁶ _____ their mothers.

3 **Write two paragraphs about children today.**

_____

_____

_____

_____

_____

_____

14

Did you have a good day?

Lesson One Words

1 Write.

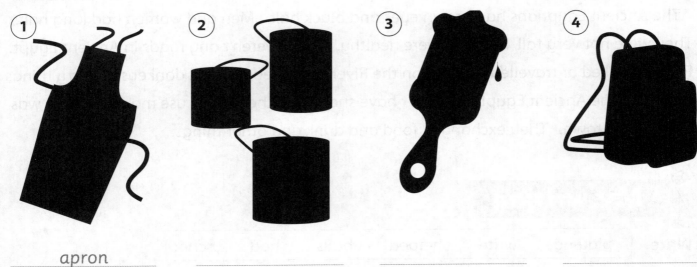

apron _____

2 Choose from the words above. Write.

1 I always use a _____paintbrush_____ in art.

2 I always wear my _____ in art.

3 I sometimes use purple _____ in art.

4 I always put my lunch in my _____.

5 I sometimes use a _____ in maths.

6 I always wear my _____ in PE.

7 I always put my school things in my _____.

8 I sometimes use a _____ in English.

1 **Circle the correct answer.** 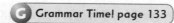 Grammar Time! page 133

Did they like the film?

Yes, they did. / (No, they didn't.)

Did he have lunch at school?

Yes, he did. / No, he didn't.

Did she use her dictionary in the
English lesson?

Yes, she did. / No, she didn't.

Did they have art today?

Yes, they did. / No, they didn't.

2 **Complete the sentences with *What*, *When* or *Where* and *did*.**

1 _What did_ your dad watch on TV?   A film.

2 _____ you have breakfast?   At eight o'clock.

3 _____ you play football?   At the sports centre.

4 _____ your mum cook for dinner?   A fish pie.

5 _____ you visit your grandpa?   On Saturday.

6 _____ you have dinner?   In a restaurant.

1 Look and write. Then answer *Yes, I did* or *No, I didn't.*   Ⓖ Grammar Time! page 133

1 Did you use __a paintbrush__ at school yesterday?
  ✓ __Yes, I did.__

2 Did you use _____ at school yesterday?
  ✗ _____

3 Did you use _____ at school yesterday?
  ✓ _____

4 Did you use _____ at school yesterday?
  ✗ _____

5 Did you use _____ at school yesterday?
  ✗ _____

2 Write. Then answer for you with *Yes, we did* or *No, we didn't.*

| have | ~~have~~ | help | like | paint | play |

Did you have a good day?

1 __Did you have__ a good day at school today?   Yes, we did.
2 _____ a picture at school today?   _____
3 _____ a new game at school today?   _____
4 _____ lots of fun at school today?   _____
5 _____ your lessons at school today?   _____
6 _____ your teacher at school today?   _____

1 **Match.**

1 boot ☐   2 moon ☐   3 tube ☐   4 glue ☐   5 tune [a]

2 **Write.**   June   blue   tube   moon   tune   ~~school~~   flute   glue

It's Tuesday night,
And I'm not at ¹ ___school___ .
I've got ² _____ and ³ _____ s,
And paint that's ⁴ _____ .
I make a toy ⁵ _____ ,
I look up at the ⁶ _____ .
It's a hot ⁷ _____ night,
And I play a ⁸ _____ .

3 **Read and number the pictures. Then write.**

1 At night, you can see the ___moon___ in the sky.

2 My brother can play a _____ on the flute.

3 A _____ is long and round.

4 You can make a cube with paper and _____ .

Reading

1 Write.

1 The r*ope*_____ holds the tent up.

2 The t_____ stops us from getting wet when it rains.

3 We can see at night with a t_____.

4 We have to light a fire with m_____.

5 My s_____ is warm at night.

6 We cook food with a f_____.

2 **Read the text in the Class Book. Circle the wrong words. Write the correct words.**

1 The campsite was near the sea.   *a river*

2 The children used rope and wood to make a tent.

3 They used matches to see in the dark.

4 There was a sheep next to their tent.

5 It rained every day.

6 The children used a stone to start a fire.

Writing

1 Circle the correct words.

Last Wednesday, we were on a school trip. We visited a museum in the morning.
¹ **First** / **Then**, we watched a DVD. ² **Finally** / **Then**, we looked at photos. ³ **First** / **Next**,
we played with old clothes and toys. ⁴ **Finally** / **Then**, we had lunch in the café.

My writing

2 Put the sentences in the correct order.

What did you do at school today?

a Next, we had a music lesson. We played the guitars together – it was great! ☐

b Finally, we played football in the playground, and I walked home with my mum. ☐

c First, I talked to my friends in the playground. [1]

d Then, we had maths with Mr Taylor. ☐

3 Write about your school day. Use time words.

| First | Then | Next | Finally |

_____

_____

_____

_____

_____

_____

_____

Lesson One Words

1 **Look and write. Find the extra word (↓) and answer the question.**

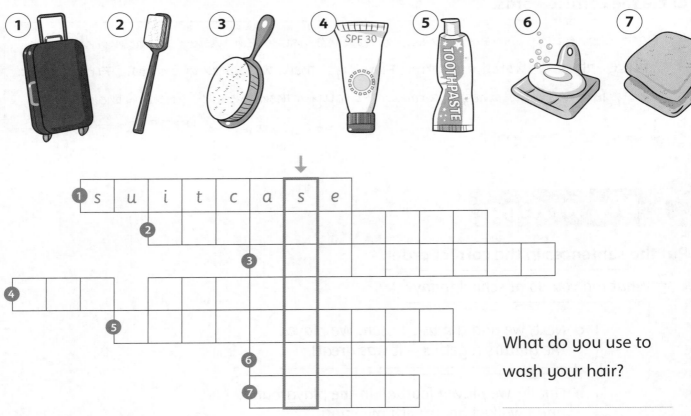

	1	s	u	i	t	c	a	s	e

What do you use to wash your hair?

_____

2 **Write.**

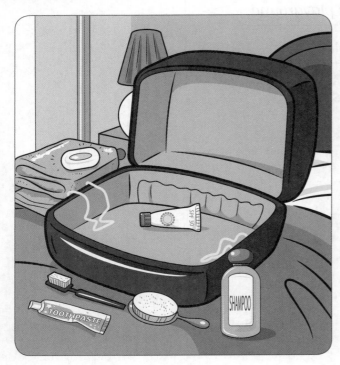

1 The ___sun cream___ is in the suitcase.

2 The towel is next to the _____.

3 The _____ is next to the shampoo.

4 The _____ is under the soap.

5 The _____ is in front of the toothbrush.

6 The _____ is on top of the towel.

7 The _____ is behind the toothpaste.

8 The hairbrush is between the toothbrush and the _____.

1 Write.  Grammar Time! page 134

1 Is he going to visit his cousins next week?   Yes, _he is_____ .

2 Are they going to swim in the sea?   No, _____ .

3 Is it going to rain tomorrow?   No, _____ .

4 Are you going to take your shampoo on holiday?   Yes, _____ .

5 Is she going to buy sun cream later?   Yes, _____ .

6 Are you going to play tennis on Tuesday?   No, _____ .

2 Complete the sentences with *going to*.

buy   have   listen   ~~make~~   play   read

1 I'm _going to make_ a cake.

2 We're _____ tennis.

3 He's _____ a book.

4 I'm _____ _____ breakfast.

5 She's _____ some shampoo.

6 They're _____ to music.

1 Look at the Class Book. Match. 🄖 Grammar Time! page 134

1 Is Alex going to take a towel?   ☐ c   **a** Yes, they are.

2 Is Emma going to take a toothbrush?   ☐   **b** No, he isn't.

3 Are Emma and Billy going to take some sun cream? ☐   **c** Yes, he is.

4 Are Alex and Tom going to take some toothpaste? ☐   **d** No, she isn't.

5 Is Tom going to take some soap?   ☐   **e** Yes, he is.

6 Is Billy going to take a hairbrush? ☐   **f** No, they aren't.

2 Write sentences with *is*, *isn't*, *are* or *aren't*.

① Alex _is going to take_ _some shampoo_ ✓.

② Emma and Billy _____ _____ ✓.

③ Billy _____ _____ ✓.

④ Alex _____ _____ ✗.

3 Write. | time   photos   going   some   to   ~~suitcase~~   go   take |

I'm going to pack my ¹ _suitcase_ ,
I'm going to ² _____ away.
I'm going to have a great ³ _____ ,
I'm going on holiday!

I'm going to ⁴ _____ some sun cream,
And also some shampoo.
I'm ⁵ _____ to take my toothbrush,
And ⁶ _____ toothpaste, too.

I'm going to take some ⁷ _____ ,
I'm going to see the sea.
I'm going ⁸ _____ swim and windsurf,
I'm going to waterski!

I'm going to pack my suitcase

1 Complete the words.

    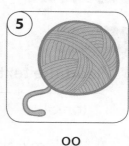

1. _w_oo_d_
2. ___oo___
3. ___oo___
4. ___oo___
5. ___oo___

2 Write. good   cook   ~~hood~~   book   wool   wood

It's a very cold day.
I've got a coat with a ¹ ___hood___.
I've got my ² _____ scarf,
And I'm feeling ³ _____.

I'm sitting on some ⁴ _____.
I'm looking at my ⁵ _____.
The book's very good.
It tells me how to ⁶ _____.

3 Read and number the pictures. Then write.

 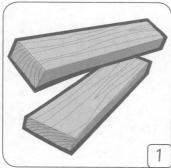  

1 You can use rope and ___wood___ to make a bridge.

2 A _____ works in a kitchen.

3 I haven't got a hat, but my jacket's got a _____.

4 I've got a ball of _____ and I want to make a scarf.

Skills Time!

Reading

1 Read the text in the Class Book and write.

> tonight   this afternoon   soon   tomorrow   later   next week

1 William and his family are going to visit the aquarium
   this afternoon .

2 They are going to see a dolphin show
   _____ .

3 William is going to try seafood _____ .

4 William is going to swim in the sea
   _____ .

5 William and his family are going to fly home _____ .

6 William and Dan are going to look at lots of photos _____ .

2 Write short answers.

1 Is Dan in Barcelona? _No, he isn't._

2 Is William having fun? _____

3 Does William's sister like sharks? _____

4 Is there a dolphin show at the aquarium? _____

5 Are there penguins at the aquarium? _____

6 Is William going to take photos? _____

3 Circle the mistakes. Write the correct words.

1 The weather is (cold) and sunny. _hot_

2 The amusement park is boring. _____

3 William and his family are going to visit the zoo
   this evening. _____

4 William's sister loves sharks. _____

5 William and his family are going to visit
   a museum tomorrow. _____

6 They are going to drive home next week. _____

Writing

1 Where do we use these words in a letter? Circle *start* or *end*.

1 Write soon.   start / (end)

2 See you soon.   start / end

3 How are you?   start / end

4 Dear …   start / end

5 Thanks for your letter. start / end

6 Bye for now.   start / end

My writing

2 Read the email. Underline the start words in red and the end words in blue.

Order the pictures and write the numbers.

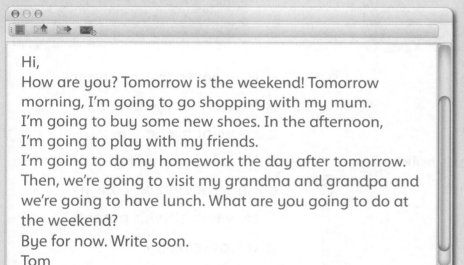

Hi,
How are you? Tomorrow is the weekend! Tomorrow morning, I'm going to go shopping with my mum. I'm going to buy some new shoes. In the afternoon, I'm going to play with my friends.
I'm going to do my homework the day after tomorrow. Then, we're going to visit my grandma and grandpa and we're going to have lunch. What are you going to do at the weekend?
Bye for now. Write soon.
Tom

3 What are you going to do this weekend? Write an email to Tom.

_____

_____

_____

_____

_____

_____

_____

Fluency Time! ⑤

1 **Look and match.**

Max

Jerry

1 Where did Max go on holiday? | b | **a** He went to the mountains.
2 Who did Max go with? | ☐ | **b** He went to the beach.
3 What was Max's holiday like? | ☐ | **c** He went hiking.
4 What was the best part of Max's holiday? | ☐ | **d** He went swimming.
5 Where did Jerry go on holiday? | ☐ | **e** He went with his cousins.
6 Who did Jerry go with? | ☐ | **f** He went with his parents.
7 What was Jerry's holiday like? | ☐ | **g** It was relaxing.
8 What was the best part of Jerry's holiday? | ☐ | **h** It was exciting.

2 **Write.**   best   ~~where~~   where   what   who

1 _Where_ did you go on holiday?   I went to London.

2 _____ did you go with?   With my sisters and my parents.

3 _____ did you stay?   We stayed in a hotel.

4 _____ was it like?   It was brilliant.

5 What was the _____ part?   We visited museums and we bought souvenirs.

1 Watch and circle.

1 Anna went to New York with **her friends** / **her parents**.

2 It was **exciting** / **brilliant**.

3 She **had** / **didn't have** a great time.

4 The best part was **shopping and sightseeing** / **shopping and sleeping**.

2 Write. Then match.

1 I / go / New York / my parents

I went to New York with my parents.

2 what / best / part / ?

3 we / buy lots of souvenirs

4 Where / you / go / ?

5 It / exciting / . / There / river / and / big lake

6 Wow! / It / look / fantastic.

3 Talk about your last holiday with a friend.

Where did you go on holiday?   *I went to the beach.*

1 **Write the school things in the backpack. Write the holiday things in the suitcase.**

shampoo   hairbrush   apron   lunch box   sun cream
toothpaste   dictionary   calculator   soap   towel   PE kit

My school things

I'm going to school tomorrow.
I'm going to put these things
in my backpack.

My holiday things

I'm going on holiday next week.
I'm going to put these things
in my suitcase.

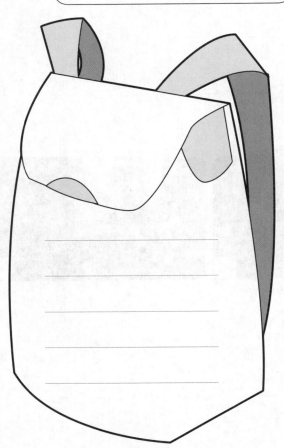

shampoo

2 **Circle the odd one out.**

1 (tent)   heavy   light   hard

2 matches   last night   sleeping bag   torch

3 later   this afternoon   rope   tonight

4 paintbrush   calculator   apron   soon

5 soft   frying pan   easy   difficult

6 towel   toothbrush   yesterday   sun cream

3 Write the correct forms of the verbs.

1 I *'m going to cook* _____ (cook) lunch tomorrow.

2 She _played_____ (play) volleyball last Saturday.

3 We _____ (listen) to my new CD yesterday.

4 He _____ (play) football next week.

5 They _____ (watch) TV tonight.

6 I _____ (cook) dinner last weekend.

4 Write one or two words to complete the sentences.

Yesterday, Dad ___*didn't work*___ in the garden. He ___*stayed*___ in the

house and he _____ to music. Mum _____ go to the

shops. She _____ a special dinner. The children _____

DVDs. They wanted to read their new books. The baby _____ with his

ball all day. They were very happy!

My work

My favourite story in Units 13–15 is _____

My favourite song in Units 13–15 is _____

My favourite unit in Units 13–15 is _____

I need to practise _____

My work in Units 13–15 is

 OK   **Good**   **Excellent**

The United Kingdom

1 Read and write. | as big as | as long as | as old as |

Hello! My name's Kira and I'm from Oxford, a city in England. Oxford is a small city – it isn't _____ London. Oxford University is famous. It's almost _____ Bologna University, the oldest university in the world.

This is the High Street in Oxford. There are lots of university buildings here. They're beautiful. The High Street and Broad Street are famous streets in Oxford. Broad Street isn't _____ the High Street, but it has beautiful buildings, too.

2 Read the Class Book. Write *T* (true) or *F* (false).

1 The Millennium Stadium isn't as modern as the Millennium Centre. ___T___

2 Princes Street in Edinburgh is almost as long as the Royal Mile. _____

3 The Tower of London isn't as old as Buckingham Palace. _____

4 Belfast is almost as big as London. _____

3 Write. | small | big | modern | old |

1 The museum is __as old as__ the library.

2 The museum isn't _____ the library.

3 The cinema is _____ the school.

4 The cinema isn't _____ the school.

5 The supermarket isn't _____ the shopping mall.

6 The supermarket is _____ the shopping mall.

7 The café is _____ the post office.

8 The café isn't _____ the post office.

Sports events

1 **Read and circle.**

The London Marathon is a running race through the streets of London. It is a race for men and women. The first race was in 1981. It is a very long race.

The runners warm up before the race. When the race starts, they run very [1] **quickly / sadly**. At the end of the race, the winner smiles [2] **loudly / happily**.

More than 30,000 people take part in the race and 1,000,000 go to London to watch the race every year. They stand in the streets and they shout [3] **loudly / slowly**. You can also sit [4] **quietly / quickly** at home and watch the race on television.

2 **Read the Class Book and write.**

fast   happily   quietly   slowly

1 At Wimbledon, people sit _____ during the matches.

2 At Wembley, the football fans shout _____ when their team scores a goal.

3 The rowers in the Boat Race make the boats move very _____ .

4 At Royal Ascot, the horses walk _____ around the 'walking ring'.

3 **Read the Class Book and write.**

1 Do the horses at Royal Ascot run slowly?

   No, they don't. They run quickly.

3 Do the football fans shout sadly when their team scores a goal?

   _____

2 Do the ball boys and ball girls work loudly?

   _____

4 Do the boats in the Boat Race go slowly?

   _____

Clothes

1   Read and circle.

a

Hi! My name's Jess and I'm nine years old.
I wear a ¹ **costume /** **uniform** to go to school:
a black ² **skirt / shoe** and a white ³ **dress / shirt**.
I like going out with my family and friends.
I wear ⁴ **a coat / a T-shirt** to go out in winter.
I wear ⁵ **smart clothes / a tracksuit** to go to
a restaurant with my mum and dad. Tomorrow,
I'm going to go to a party. I'm going to wear
my ⁶ **favourite top / old jeans**. It's new!

b

Hello! I'm Brendan and I'm ten. I like wearing casual
clothes. In summer, I wear ¹ **shorts and a T-shirt /**
a scarf to play tennis or volleyball. I wear ² **a tracksuit /**
smart clothes to help my dad in the garden.
Last month, Dad and I painted my bedroom, and I
wore ³ **my favourite shirt / old clothes**! My school
⁴ **uniform / tie** is grey ⁵ **trousers / clothes** and a white
shirt. I also wear a blue and yellow ⁶ **tie / shoe**.

2   Read the Class Book and match the sentence halves.

1	Robbie wears a jumper	b	a to act in plays.
2	Gemma wears a uniform	☐	b to keep warm in the winter.
3	Gemma wears a skirt and a pretty top	☐	c to relax.
4	Ben wears tracksuits	☐	d to go to school.
5	Lisa wears jeans with colourful tops	☐	e to visit her grandparents at the weekend.
6	Lisa wears costumes	☐	f to hang out with her friends.

120   Culture   Clothes

Fluency Time! 1

I like painting!	So do I!
I don't like skateboarding.	Neither do I.
I love fishing.	I don't. I prefer reading comics.

Fluency Time! 2

She's very good at swimming.	He's bad at maths.
He's quite good at snorkelling.	I'm terrible at cooking.

Fluency Time! 3

Excuse me. Where's the cinema?	It's in Green Street. It's next to the museum. You can't miss it.
Can you tell me the way to Green Street, please?	Sure. Turn left at the post office. Go straight on, then turn right into Green Street.

Fluency Time! 4

That's Sam. Do you know him?	No, I don't. But I know that he goes to my school.
What's Sam like? He looks shy.	I think he's sometimes shy. But he's very nice.

Fluency Time! 5

Where did you go on holiday?	I went to New York with my family.
Wow! Lucky you! What was it like?	It was brilliant! I had a great time.
What was the best part?	We went sightseeing and shopping. We bought lots of souvenirs. Here's one for you!
Cool! Thanks!	

Fluency Time!

1 Play and say. Write.

4 Go forward **3**

5 What was the best part of your holiday?

I / stayed / tent

6 Go back **1**

7

8 Go forward **1**

I / very good / skateboarding

9

Can / tell / me / way / cinema?

17 I / know / Paul / very kind and generous.

Excuse me. Where's the sports centre?

Go / straight /can't / miss it.

18

You are the winner!

Grammar Time!

Unit 1 Present simple with *be*

affirmative	
I'm	from Egypt.
You're	from Spain.
He's	from Thailand.
She'___	from the USA.
We're	from Australia.
They're	_____ Brazil.

questions			
Where	**am I**	from?	
Where	**are you**	_____	?
_____	**is he**	from?	
Where	**is she**	from?	
Where	**are** _____	from?	
Where	**are they**	from?	

1 Complete.

1 Where is she from?   _____She's_____ from the USA.

2 Where are Tom and Jane from?   _____ from Australia.

3 Where _____ from?   He's from Spain.

4 Where _____ from?   We're from Thailand.

Unit 2 *like / don't like + ing*

affirmative		
I	_like_	play**ing** volleyball.
You	**like**	skateboard**ing**.
He	**likes**	play_____ football.
_____	**like**	do**ing** gymnastics.
They	**like**	tak_____ photos.

negative		
I	**don't like**	fish**ing**.
You	**don't like**	play_____ basketball.
_____	**doesn't like**	tak**ing** photos.
We	**don't like**	play**ing** volleyball.
They	**don't** _____	read**ing** comics.

1 Complete the sentences. (✗ = not like, ✓ = like)

1 They _don't like_ doing gymnastics. (✗)   2 He _____ playing basketball. (✓)

3 We _____ skateboarding. (✓)   4 You _____ reading comics. (✗)

5 I _____ taking photos. (✓)   6 She _____ fishing. (✗)

Questions with *Do* / *Does*

questions			short answers	
<u>Do</u>	I like	tak**ing** photos?	**Yes**, I **do**. / **No**, I <u>don't</u> .	
Do	you like	play_____ chess?	**Yes**, you **do**. / **No**, _____ **don't**.	
Does	she like	skateboard**ing**?	_____ , she **does**. / **No**, she **doesn't**.	
Do	_____ like	fish**ing**?	**Yes**, we _____ . / **No**, we **don't**.	
Do	they _____	do**ing** gymnastics?	**Yes**, they **do**. / _____ , they **don't**.	

2 Complete the questions with *Do* or *Does*. Then write short answers that are true for you.

1 <u>Do</u> you like doing gymnastics? _____

2 _____ your mum and dad like taking photos? _____

3 _____ your best friend like skateboarding? _____

4 _____ you like playing chess? _____

5 _____ you like going to the park? _____

6 _____ your friends like fishing? _____

Unit 3 *your* / *our* / *their*

You've got a CD player.	**Your** CD player is big.
We've got a camera.	**Our** camera is small.
They've got a computer.	**Their** computer is new.

1 Complete the sentences with *your, our* or *their*.

1 We've got a new DVD player. <u>Our</u> new DVD player is small.

2 Lisa and Jim are playing with _____ friends.

3 Can you put on _____ coat, please?

4 We're reading _____ books together.

5 Can I use _____ camera, please?

6 The children are using _____ new computer.

can / can't

questions			short answers
Can	I	**use** your computer?	**Yes**, I **can**. / _____ , I **can't**.
_____	you	**turn off** the TV?	_____ , you **can**. / **No**, you **can't**.
Can	he	**read** a book?	**Yes**, he **can**. / **No**, he _____ .
Can	they	**listen** to a CD?	**Yes**, they _____ . / **No**, they **can't**.

2 Complete the questions. Then write the answers. (X = no, ✓ = yes)

| have   close   listen   read   turn |

1 ___Can___ I ___read___ your book, please? (X)   ___No, you can't.___

2 _____ he _____ off the computer? (✓)   _____

3 _____ we _____ the window? (✓)   _____

4 _____ she _____ to a CD? (X)   _____

5 _____ they _____ dinner at our house? (X)   _____

Unit 4 Present continuous (*be* verb + *ing*)

affirmative	
I'm	swim**ming**.
You**'re**	sail_____ .
She**'s**	surf**ing**.
_____ **'re**	kayak**ing**.
They**'re**	windsurf**ing**.

negative	
I**'m not**	snorkel**ling**.
You **aren't**	waterski**ing**.
She **isn't**	swim_____ .
We **aren't**	div**ing**.
_____ **aren't**	sail**ing**.

1 Write sentences.

1 I'm diving.   ___I'm not sailing.___   (not sail)

2 She's snorkelling.   _____   (not waterski)

3 They're eating.   _____   (not play)

4 We aren't sleeping.   _____   (read)

5 You aren't windsurfing.   _____   (surf)

Unit 5   Present continuous questions and short answers

questions			short answers
Am	I	read**ing**?	**Yes**, I _am_ . / **No**, I'm **not**.
Are	you	paint**ing**?	**Yes**, you **are**. / _____, you **aren't**.
Is	she	eat**ing**?	_____, she **is**. / **No**, she **isn't**.
Are	_____	shop**ping**?	**Yes**, we **are**. / **No**, we **aren't**.
Are	they	fly_____?	**Yes**, _____ **are**. / **No**, they **aren't**.

1 Complete the questions. Then write short answers.   (**✗** = no, **✓** = yes)

1 __Are__ they windsurfing? (**✗**)   _No, they aren't._
2 _____ she snorkelling? (**✓**)   _____
3 _____ I surfing? (**✓**)   _____
4 _____ he diving? (**✗**)   _____
5 _____ you swimming? (**✗**)   _____

Unit 6   Present simple

affirmative				negative		
I	**have**	a shower at night.		I	_don't have_	a shower in the morning.
You	**get**	up early.		_____	**don't get**	up late.
_____	**works**	on a farm.		He	**doesn't work**	in a school.
We	**walk**	to school.		_____	**don't walk**	home.
They	_____	the bus.		They	_____ **catch**	the train.

1 Complete the sentences.

1 You have breakfast in the morning. You _don't have_ dinner in the morning.
2 She doesn't live in the UK. She _____ in Brazil.
3 We finish school at three o'clock. We _____ school at four o'clock.
4 I don't do my homework in the morning. I _____ my homework at night.
5 He gets up at seven o'clock. He _____ at eight o'clock.
6 They don't walk to school. They _____ the bus.

Present simple questions and short answers

questions				short answers
Do	I	**walk**	to school?	**Yes**, I **do**. / **No**, I **don't**.
Do	you	**live**	in Russia?	**Yes**, you **do**. / _____, you **don't**.
Does	_____	**work**	in a school?	_____, she **does**. / **No**, she **doesn't**.
_____	we	**catch**	the bus?	**Yes**, _____ **do**. / **No**, we **don't**.
Do	they	**get**	up early?	**Yes**, they _____. / **No**, they _____.

2 Complete the questions. Then write short answers. (✗ = no, ✓ = yes)

1 ___Does___ he get up at eight o'clock? (✗)   ___No, he doesn't.___

2 _____ we have breakfast with our family? (✓)   _____

3 _____ she live in a small house? (✓)   _____

4 _____ they walk to school? (✗)   _____

Unit 7   Adverbs of frequency: *always, sometimes, never*

I **always** get up at eight o'clock.
He **sometimes** watches TV in the morning.
They **never** go to bed late.

1 Order the words. Write true sentences about you. Use *always*, *sometimes* or *never*.

1 have / family. / I / with / breakfast / my   *I always have breakfast with my family.*

2 homework / in / I / my / do / the morning. _____

3 at / brush / I / my / teeth / night. _____

Prepositions of time: *on, at, in*

He doesn't work **on** Saturdays.   I get up **at** eight o'clock.   We don't go to school **in** August.

2 Complete the questions with *on*, *at* or *in*. Then answer the questions.

1 Do you go to school ___in___ February?   Yes, I do.

2 Does school start _____ nine o'clock?   _____

3 Do you get up late _____ Saturdays?   _____

4 Is your birthday _____ November?

Unit 8 Countable and uncountable nouns with *a*, *an* and *some*

affirmative		
I 'd like	a	sandwich.
You**'d like**	an	orange.
She**'d** _____	some	rice.
We**'d like**	some	apples.
_____ **'d like**	some	cereal.

questions		
Would I **like**	a	sandwich?
_____ you **like**	an	orange?
Would she **like**	some	rice?
Would we _____	some	apples?
Would they **like**	some	cereal?

1 Write *a*, *an* or *some*.

1 _some_ rice   2 _____ apple   3 _____ bananas

4 _____ water   5 _____ lemon   6 _____ bread

7 _____ biscuit 8 _____ oranges   9 _____ cereal

10 _____ meat   11 _____ melon   12 _____ egg

Unit 9 Comparatives and superlatives

comparative			
Colin is	fast**er than**		Billy.
An apple is		_____ **than**	a melon.
The USA is	big**ger**	_____	Spain.

superlative		
Tom is	**the** _fastest_ .	
A grape is	**the** small**est**.	
Russia is	_____	big**gest** country.

1 Complete the sentences with comparatives and superlatives.

1 Carl is _____ _shorter_ _____ (short) than Fred.

2 Adam is _____ (tall) than Carl.

3 Fred is the _____ (tall).

4 Mice are _____ (small) than elephants.

5 Cheetahs are _____ (big) than mice.

6 Elephants are the _____ (big).

7 A car is _____ (slow) than a plane.

8 A plane is the _____ (fast).

Unit 10 *must / mustn't*

affirmative		
You	must	walk on the path.
We	_____	play in the playground.

negative		
We	**mustn't**	walk on the grass.
They	_____	play in the fountain.

1 Write *must* or *mustn't*.

School rules

1 You ___mustn't___ read comics at school.

2 You _____ listen to the teacher.

3 You _____ talk in class.

4 You _____ ride your bike in the playground.

Unit 11 *There was / were, There wasn't / weren't*

There **was** a park in our town a hundred years ago.
There **were** trams in our town a hundred years ago.
There **wasn't** a supermarket in our town a hundred years ago.
There **weren't** any cars in our town a hundred years ago.

lots of, some, any

There were **lots of** cheese sandwiches.
There were **some** tomato sandwiches.
There weren't **any** chicken sandwiches.

1 Circle the correct words.

1 There **were** / **was** lots of flowers.

2 There **wasn't** / **weren't** a fountain.

3 There **was** / **were** a playground.

4 There **was** / **were** lots of trees.

Time words and phrases

| Yesterday | Last week | Last year | Last Monday | Two years ago | Then |

2 Complete the sentences. Write about you.

1 Yesterday, I _____ .

2 Last week, _____ .

3 Two years ago, _____ .

4 Then, _____ .

5 Last year, _____ .

6 Last Monday, _____ .

Unit 12   Past simple: *be*

affirmative		
I	_was_	short.
You	**were**	worried.
_____	**was**	young.
We	**were**	cheerful.
_____	**were**	friendly.

negative		
I	**wasn't**	tall.
_____	**weren't**	relaxed.
She	**wasn't**	old.
_____	**weren't**	miserable.
They	**weren't**	shy.

1 Complete the sentences.

1 There were sandwiches at the party. They ___weren't___ very big. (**✗**)

2 I _____ hungry last night. (**✓**)

3 You _____ happy on holiday. (**✓**)

4 There was a boy in the park. He _____ friendly. (**✗**)

5 We _____ at school last week. (**✗**)

6 Last year, I _____ shy in class. (**✓**)

7 Yesterday, it _____ windy, but it was wet. (**✗**)

8 You _____ in class yesterday. (**✗**)

Past simple: *have*

affirmative		
I	**had**	pizza for lunch yesterday.
You	_____	a guitar lesson last Friday.
He	**had**	cereal for breakfast yesterday.
We	_____	an art lesson yesterday.
They	**had**	a picnic last week.

negative		
I	*didn't have*	sandwiches.
You	**didn't have**	a piano lesson.
He	**didn't** _____	bread.
We	**didn't have**	a music lesson.
They	_____ **have**	a party.

2 Complete the sentences so that they are true for you.

Yesterday …

1 I _____ a music lesson.
2 I _____ sandwiches for lunch.
3 I _____ cereal for breakfast.
4 I _____ dinner with my family.

Unit 13   Past simple with regular verbs

affirmative		
I	**started**	my homework at six o'clock.
_____	**worked**	in a school last year.
She	**wanted**	a camera for her birthday.
He	**laughed**	at the cartoon.
We	**used**	a camera on holiday.
They	_____	football last weekend.

negative		
I	*didn't start*	it at five o'clock.
You	**didn't work**	on a farm.
_____	**didn't want**	a bike.
He	**didn't** _____	at the film.
We	_____ **use**	a computer.
They	**didn't play**	basketball.

1 Write sentences about Jim using the past simple affirmative and negative.

1 finish / his homework / Sunday (✓)   *He finished his homework on Sunday.*

2 love / his dinner / Saturday (✓)   _____

3 cook / fish pie / Saturday (✗)   _____

4 hate / his dinner / Sunday (✗)   _____

Unit 14 Past simple questions and answers

questions				short answers
Did	I	**walk**	to school yesterday?	**Yes**, I **did**. / **No**, _____ **didn't**.
Did	you	**have**	lunch at school?	**Yes**, you **did**. / _____ , you **didn't**.
Did	she	**paint**	a picture?	**Yes**, she _____ . / **No**, _____ **didn't**.
Did	_____	**play**	tennis?	**Yes**, we **did**. / **No**, we _____ .
_____	they	**visit**	their cousins?	**Yes**, _____ **did**. / **No**, they **didn't**.

1 Complete the questions and write short answers that are true for you.

have	eat	listen	paint	~~walk~~	visit

1 ___Did___ you ___walk___ to school yesterday? _____

2 _____ you _____ a picture yesterday? _____

3 _____ you _____ to music yesterday? _____

4 _____ you _____ a picnic yesterday? _____

5 _____ you _____ rice for lunch yesterday? _____

6 _____ you _____ your grandma last week? _____

Past simple questions with *What*, *Where* and *When*

What _did_ you have for lunch?	Sandwiches and grapes.
When _____ he visit his cousin?	Last weekend.
Where _____ we play tennis?	In the park.

2 Complete the questions.

1 ___What___ did you have for dinner last night?   Pizza.

2 _____ did you have dinner?   At home.

3 _____ did you have dinner?   At seven o'clock.

4 _____ did you have lunch yesterday?   At school.

5 _____ did you have lunch?   At one o'clock.

6 _____ did you have for lunch?   Sandwiches and an orange.

Unit 15   be going to

affirmative		
I'm	_going to_	buy a hairbrush.
You're	**going to**	have lunch.
He's	**going to**	play tennis.
We're	_____	visit friends.
_____ 're	**going to**	watch a DVD.

negative		
I'm not	**going to**	buy a toothbrush.
You **aren't**	_____	have dinner.
_____ **isn't**	**going to**	play football.
We **aren't**	**going to**	visit our cousins.
They **aren't**	_____	watch a play.

1   **Complete the sentences.**   (**✗** = no, **✓** = yes)

> buy   ~~have~~   visit   watch

1   We _aren't going to have_ _____ a picnic. (**✗**)
2   They _____ their grandma. (**✓**)
3   She _____ sun cream. (**✓**)
4   You _____ TV. (**✗**)

Questions with *be going to*

questions				short answers
Am I	**going to**		go on holiday?	**Yes**, I _am_ . / **No**, I'm not.
Are you	_____		take your suitcase?	**Yes**, you **are**. / **No**, you **aren't**.
Is it	**going to**		rain?	**Yes**, it _____ . / _____ , it **isn't**.
Are _____	**going to**		swim in the sea?	_____ , we **are**. / **No**, we **aren't**.
Are they	_____		make a cake?	**Yes**, they _____ . / **No**, they **aren't**.

2   **Complete the sentences so that they are true for you.**

> brush   ~~go~~   play   read

1   I'm _going to go_ _____ to school tomorrow.
2   I'm _____ computer games next week.
3   _____ my teeth later.
4   _____ a book on Saturday.

Word List

Starter
April
August
aunt
brother
cousin
dad
December
eighty
February
fifty
forty
grandma
grandpa
January
July
June
March
May
mum
ninety
November
October
one hundred
September
seventy
sister
sixty
ten
thirty
twenty
uncle

Unit 1
Australia
autumn
Brazil

crayon
draw
drink (v)
Egypt
garden
play (v)
Russia
season
Spain
spoon
spring
straw
summer
Thailand
(the) UK
(the) USA
winter

Unit 2
bike
cook (v)
cube
do gymnastics
face
fish (v)
June
kite
paint (v)
play basketball
play chess
play the guitar
play the piano
play volleyball
read comics
rope
shop (v)
skateboard (v)

space
stone
take photos
visit (family)

Unit 3
badges
camera
car
CD player
comics
computer
DVD player
MP3 player
park
postcards
posters
scarf
shark
shells
star
stickers
turn off …
turn on …
TV

Unit 4
ball
beautiful
clean
dangerous
dive (v)
kayak (v)
mall
polluted
safe
sail (v)

small
snorkel (v)
surf (v)
swim (v)
tall
ugly
under
wall
waterski (v)
windsurf (v)

Unit 5
angry
camel
corn
crocodile
flamingo
fork
free
funny
horse
kangaroo
kind
lizard
monkey
paw
penguin
scared
sorry
straw
yawn (v)
zebra

Unit 6
at the weekend
boy
brush my hair /
   teeth
catch the bus
coin
every day
finally
first
get dressed
get up (late /
   early)
have a shower
have breakfast
next
oil
oyster
soil
then
toy
walk to school

Unit 7
actor
brown
café
cinema
clown
concert
cow
film (n)
flower
house
library
mouse
museum

play (n)
playground
shopping mall
shout
singer
sports centre
swimming pool
theatre
trousers

Unit 8
adult
belt
bread
butter
cereal
cheese
child
cucumber
field
lemon
meat
melon
onion
pasta
peas
pepper
potato
quilt
salt
shield

Unit 9
big
bridge
building
camp
country

deep
high
lake
lamp
long
mountain
ocean
old
plant
pond
river
sand
tent
waterfall
wide

Unit 10
bin (n)
case
catch
chase
cross
flowers
fountain
grass
laugh
litter
meet
Monday
path
playground
race (n)
rain (n)
shout (v)
train
tray
trees

Unit 11
along
at the top of
between
bus
dream
ferry
green
happy
helicopter
ice cream
in the middle of
inside
jelly
lolly
motorbike
plane
queen
taxi
through
train
tram

Unit 12
cheerful
dry
friendly
generous
handsome
light (adj)
mean
miserable
night
old
pretty
relaxed
shine (v)
shy

sky
smile
tall
worried
young

Unit 13
coat
difficult
easy
elbow
finish
hard
hate
heavy
laugh
light (adj)
live
love
nose
snow
soap
soft
start
stone
use (v)
want

Unit 14
apron
backpack
blue
boot
calculator
dictionary
frying pan
glue
have lessons

lunch box
matches (n)
moon
paint (n)
paintbrush
PE kit
rope
sleeping bag
tent
torch
tube
tune (n)

Unit 15
book
cook (n)
good
hairbrush
hat
hood
later
next week
shampoo
soap
soon
suitcase
sun cream
this afternoon
tomorrow
tonight
toothbrush
toothpaste
towel
wood
wool